Genetic Syndromes in Communication Disorders

Genetic Syndromes
in Communication Disorders

■ *by Jack H. Jung, M.D.*

Director
Regional Medical Genetics Centre
University of Western Ontario
London, Ontario, Canada

in collaboration with: ■

Jean-Pierre Gagne, Ph.D.
Assistant Professor, Department of Communicative Disorders and
Department of Otolaryngology, University of Western Ontario

Anne L. Godden, M.Sc.
Instructor and Coordinator, Department of Communicative Disorders,
University of Western Ontario

Herbert A. Leeper, Jr., Ph.D.
Assistant Professor, Department of Communicative Disorders; Clinical Assistant
Professor, Department of Otolaryngology; Honorary Instructor, Faculty of Dentistry,
University of Western Ontario

Jerald B. Moon, Ph.D.
Research Scientist, Department of Speech Pathology and Audiology;
Adjunct Assistant Professor of Speech-Language Pathology;
University of Iowa, Iowa City, Iowa

Richard C. Seewald, Ph.D.
Assistant Professor of Audiology, Department of Communicative Disorders,
University of Western Ontario

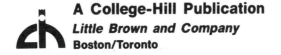
A College-Hill Publication
Little Brown and Company
Boston/Toronto

College-Hill press
A Division of
Little, Brown and Company (Inc.)
34 Beacon Street
Boston, Massachusetts 02108

Library of Congress Cataloging in Publication Data
Main entry under title:

Genetic syndromes in communication disorders / [edited] by Jack H.
    Jung ; in collaboration with J-P. Gagne . . . [et al.].
        p.   cm.
    Bibliography.
    Includes index.
    1. Genetic disorders.   2. Communicative disorders — Genetic
aspects.   I. Jung, Jack H., 1952-   .   II. Gagne, J.-P. (Jean
-Pierre)
    RB155.5.G46   1989
    616.85′5042—dc19   88-18728
                                                                                        CIP

ISBN 0-316-47695-1

Printed in the United States of America

Contents

Cross Reference Index

This index may help determine a clinical diagnosis. Fairly common dysmorphic features are listed with corresponding syndromes in which the characteristic is a frequent finding. The syndrome features are arranged under the following anatomical categories:

■ Central Nervous System/Mental Deficiency

■ Skull

■ Face

■ Eyes

■ Gastrointestinal

■ Kidneys

■ Genitals/Groin

■ Endocrine

■ Obesity

In recent years, general awareness of the importance of genetic influences on human health and disease has dramatically increased. Terms such as gene, chromosome, and recombinant DNA are being discussed more frequently in relationship to clinical and research problems. The applied health sciences, especially those disciplines involved with speech, language, and hearing, are no exception. Individuals and families seeking help for diagnoses and management are also asking questions regarding genetic recurrence risks and etiology.

It is hoped that students, teachers, and practitioners in the applied health sciences will utilize this book as a reference guide to genetic syndromes involving speech, language, and hearing problems. The introductory chapter reviews the basic principles of medical genetics. A glossary of genetic and medical terms is included in this book to minimize the need to refer to other texts or a dictionary. Users of this book may also find the cross reference index of syndromes by physical abnormality useful in arriving at a differential diagnosis.

This book is not intended as a comprehensive review of all genetic syndromes involving communication disorders. It does highlight those syndromes that we feel are seen in many interdisciplinary clinics. The sections dealing with each syndrome contain general diagnostic and management guidelines. It should be emphasized that few patients will fulfill all of the diagnostic criteria of a "classic" textbook case of a syndrome. Also, the uniqueness of each individual mandates that management be specialized accordingly.

It became apparent during the writing of this book that with many syndromes, data are lacking regarding syndrome-specific characteristics related to communication competence. There is a general paucity of information from application of current research methodologies to specific syndromes. It is hoped the book will serve as a stimulus for increased collaborative research in the area of genetic-related communication disorders. With such research, we should be able to look forward to further advances in diagnosis, management, and possible preventative strategies.

Acknowledgments

There are many people to thank for their help in the preparation of this book. Special thanks go to Dr. Daniel Ling, who was the inspiration for this work. It was through his encouragement that our group of writers came together as a team keenly interested in furthering the knowledge of ourselves and others in the complex area of genetics and communication disorders. His deep experience in the applied health sciences was invaluable as he reviewed each draft of the developing manuscript.

The members of the Department of Paediatrics and the Regional Medical Genetics Centre of the University of Western Ontario have always offered encouragement and support for this project. The support staff who deserve special mention are Susan Myers, Deborah Isaacson, Bonnie Bester–Montminy, and Kathy Baker, whose word-processing wizardry and extreme patience made the project run smoothly. For the superb illustrations, which are such an important part of this book, acknowledgment goes to Jane Lee Ling, an exceptional artist and person.

Finally, grateful appreciation goes to my wife, Eleanor, for her continued nurturance and understanding.

Jean-Pierre Gagne, Ph.D., is an Assistant Professor in the Department of Communicative Disorders and the Department of Otolaryngology at the University of Western Ontario. He obtained a M.Sc. (Applied) in Audiology and Aural Rehabilitation from McGill University and a Ph.D. in Communication Sciences from the Central Institute for the Deaf (Washington University), St. Louis. Before accepting his present academic position, Dr. Gagne worked in a rehabilitation center for hearing impaired individuals in Montreal. In addition, he taught graduate courses in Diagnostic Audiology and Aural Rehabilitation at McGill University and the University of Montreal. His research interests include the auditory perception abilities of hearing impaired individuals and aural rehabilitation. He, along with Richard Seewald, contributed the sections on hearing deficits arising from each syndrome.

Anne L. Godden, M.Sc. (Applied), is an instructor and coordinator of the clinical program in the Department of Communicative Disorders, University of Western Ontario. She received her Masters degree in Speech–Language Pathology from McGill University. Her areas of specialization include fluency disorders in children and adults and clinical supervision. She contributed the chapter on stuttering.

Jack H. Jung, M.D., F.R.C.P.(C), F.C.C.M.G., D.A.B.M.G, is presently the Director of the Regional Medical Genetics Centre of the University of Western Ontario. After receiving his M.D. degree from the University of Calgary, his postgraduate training included fellowship work in medical genetics at the University of Washington, Seattle. He has received his Fellowship from the Royal College of Physicians and Surgeons (Paediatrics), and the Canadian College of Medical Geneticists. He is also a Diplomate of the American Board of Medical Genetics. As a clinician and teacher his expertise is related to medical genetics and problems of growth and development. His research interests vary from molecular genetics studies to genetic syndromology-dysmorphology. He supervised the writing of this book and contributed the sections pertaining to medical genetics.

Herbert A. Leeper, Jr., Ph.D., is an Associate Professor in the Department of Communicative Disorders, Clinical Assistant Professor, Department of Otolaryngology, and an Honorary Instructor, Faculty of Dentistry, the University of Western Ontario. He received his Ph.D. degree from Purdue University. He is a Speech–Language Pathologist with extensive clinical, teaching and research experience with children and adults with oro-facial anomalies. He serves as a Consultant to the Thames Valley Children's Centre, Cleft Palate Team, the Maxillofacial Team, Victoria Hospital, the Oro-Facial Rehabilitation Unit, University Hospital, and the Vocal Function Laboratory, Victoria Hospital. A Fellow of the American Speech–Language–Hearing Association, he is also a member of the American Cleft Palate Association and the Canadian Craniofacial Society. He, along with Dr. Moon, contributed the sections on speech and language problems in each syndrome.

Jerald B. Moon, Ph.D., is a Research Scientist with the Department of Speech Pathology and Audiology, and an Adjunct Assistant Professor of Speech–Language Pathology, University of Iowa. He obtained his Ph.D. degree from Purdue University. He has held positions as Director of Rehabilitation Research, Thames Valley Children's Centre, and Research Scientist, Cleft Palate Program Project, University of Iowa. He is a speech scientist with extensive research and teaching experience with adults and children with oro-facial defects. Dr. Moon is a member of the American Cleft Palate Association and the American Speech–Language–Hearing Association. He, along with Dr. Leeper, contributed the sections on speech and language problems.

Richard C. Seewald, Ph.D., is an Assistant Professor of Audiology, Department of Communicative Disorders, University of Western Ontario. Dr. Seewald received his graduate degrees in Audiology from the University of Minnesota and the University of Connecticut. He has worked as a clinican in pediatric and educational settings and teaches in the areas of pediatric audiology, amplification and audiological managment of hearing impaired children. In recent years his research has been related to amplification for hearing impaired children. He, along with Dr. Gagne, contributed to the sections on hearing deficits.

Chapter 1

Principles of Medical Genetics

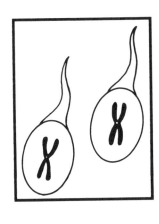

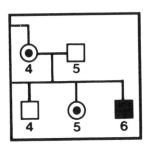

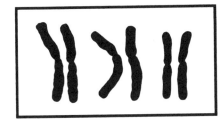

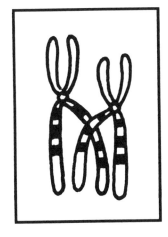

A common misconception is that a medical geneticist only deals with extremely rare diseases. Unfortunately, genetic diseases are not uncommon. It is estimated that three to four percent of all children are born with a major genetic or congenital disease. Surveys of children performed at one year of age suggest that as many as 10 percent will have problems of genetic etiology. Included in these statistics will be many of the disorders involving speech-language difficulties or hearing impairment.

With greater frequency, patients and their families are confronting health care professionals with questions regarding causation. Some of these concerns center around the possible role of prenatal exposure to potentially harmful environmental factors. Others also question the relative contribution of genetic familial factors in the pathophysiology of a disease process. This is the situation where the clinical geneticist may play an important role.

A clinical geneticist does more than impart recurrence risk figures to couples who have already had an affected child. Although this is an important aspect of the genetic counseling process, there are other critical points to consider. The clinical geneticist, utilizing skills in history taking and physical examination, can help in arriving at an accurate diagnosis. The importance of a correct diagnosis cannot be overemphasized, as it will determine the information given to families and influence practical aspects of management.

After a diagnosis is reached, it must be shared with the family or individual in an empathetic manner. Very often, this type of information has been long overdue. Even if the implications of the diagnosis are not entirely optimistic, parents finally have "an answer" and are often relieved. This may, in certain situations, also alleviate feelings of guilt or uncertainty regarding prenatal factors such as the potential influence of diet and drugs.

With a diagnosis, there is also the benefit of the experience of others with the same problem. This can help in determining prognosis and aspects of management. If there are associated potential problems, steps can be taken for early detection and treatment. Often, the expertise of other members of a multidisciplinary team is enlisted. This may include other medical specialists, clinicians involved with speech and hearing, special educators, public health nurses, and social workers. In order for optimal help to be provided, all concerned should be familiar with the information provided here, relating to the description of various *phenotypes,* the complex interactions between *genotypes* (genetic factors), and the *environment.*

This discussion of genetic principles will be framed around the three major categories of chromosomal, single gene, and polygenic-multifactorial factors related to diseases.

CHROMOSOMAL. Chromosomally determined diseases are those that (1) are produced by microscopically detectable cytogenetic aberrations (numerical or structural, of autosomes or sex chromosomes); (2) arise during gamete formation or shortly after fertilization; (3) most frequently appear in families by *de novo* events and are not inherited (exceptions to this are certain structural rearrangements).

SINGLE GENE. Sometimes referred to as *monogenic,* single gene diseases are transmitted according to Mendelian laws of inheritance. This group consists of a large number of rare diseases, syndromes, or morphological traits. the 1986 edition of McKusick's catalogue, *Mendelian Inheritance in Man,* lists 3,907 variant clinical phenotypes, of which approximately three-quarters are associated with impairment of health. These dominant, recessive, or X-linked conditions may be associated with a high risk of recurrence. Many of the conditions discussed in this book fall under this category of genetic causation.

POLYGENIC-MULTIFACTORIAL. Diseases that are polygenetic-multifactorial (1) include relatively common developmental defects, (2) have familial occurrence that cannot be attributed to chance alone or solely to the action of environmental influences, and (3) have patterns of transmission that do not follow Mendelian laws of inheritance. The polygenic disorders include many birth defects such as congenital heart disease, anencephaly, spina bifida, and cleft lip and/or cleft palate.

Incidence and Prevalence of Genetic Disease

Genetic abnormalities affect a large segment of the population:

■ In live births, 0.5 percent have chromosomal aberrations and one percent have single gene mutations.

■ Over 10 percent of individuals are at risk, later in life, for disease of genetic cause. Of the conditions discussed in this book, the features of speech and language problems or hearing impairment may be of late onset or detection.

■ Patients with genetic syndromes need to seek the expertise of multidisciplinary health care teams. Research surveys show that the average prevalence of genetic disease in children admitted to referral centers is over 50 percent.

■ Fewer studies have been done on adults, but the estimated prevalence of genetic disease (12 to 16 percent) is almost certainly an underestimate.

■ One-half of all recorded pediatric deaths probably have a genetic cause.

■ The Human Chromosomes

The word *chromosome* comes from the Greek *chromos,* meaning colored and *soma,* meaning body. Chromosomes are present in all nucleated cells and contain the genetic information encoded by functional units of DNA called *genes.* DNA is arranged in complex association with scaffold proteins and nucleosomes. This efficient method of compaction allows DNA to be packaged for cell division.

Each species has a characteristic chromosome constitution referred to as the chromosome *karyotype.* Normal human somatic cells contain 46 chromosomes composed of 23 pairs (one of each pair from the mother's egg and the other from the father's sperm).

Cytogenetics

Cytogenetics refers to the study of chromosomes. This can most conveniently be carried out in samples of peripheral blood lymphocytes, but almost any growing tissue can be used (e.g., bone marrow, peritoneum, skin fibroblasts, amniotic fluid cells, chorion frondosum).

Chromosomes may be identified with numerous stains, each one resulting in a different banding pattern, which presumably is the result of variations in physical or chemical structure (see Figure 1–1). The 23 homologous pairs are divided into the autosomes (number 1 to 22 inclusive) and the sex chromosomes (XX female; XY = male).

Morphologically, chromosomes have a narrow waist called a *centromere* which allows for further classification. The short arm is called *p,* and the long arm *q* (see Figure 1–2).

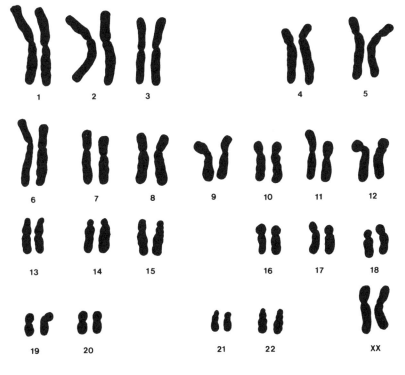

FIGURE 1–1:
Female chromosome karyotype (46,XX); solid staining.

Mitosis and Meiosis

Centromere

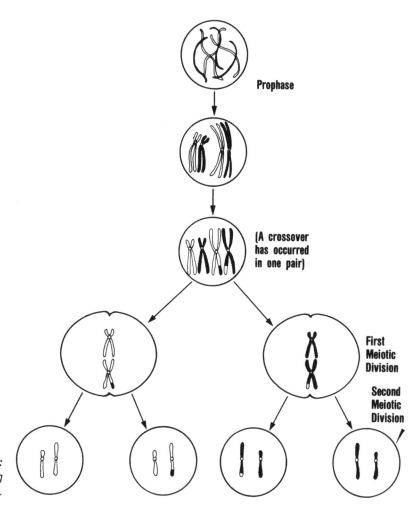

FIGURE 1-2:
Three different types of human chromosomes differing in centromere placement. From left to right: metacentric, submetacentric, and acrocentric.

Following conception, the zygote divides and multiplies to form the embryo by a process of cell division called *mitosis*. In this type of cell division, one cell produces two identical daughter cells (with, not surprisingly, identical genetic information). This division is the common mechanism for growth and development.

Meiosis is that cell division found only in the gonads and is associated with the formation of either sperm or eggs. It is responsible for maintaining a constant number of chromosomes from one generation to the next (see Figure 1-3).

Each gonadal cell involved in meiosis eventually ends up forming four cells. These daughter cells end up with half as many chromosomes as the parent cell. The process by which this is accomplished is complex. Initially, the chromosomes become duplicated before the prophase stage of meiosis. This is the stage when they become visible as double stranded structures, each

Prophase

(A crossover has occurred in one pair)

First Meiotic Division

Second Meiotic Division

FIGURE 1-3:
Events that occur during meiosis.

strand being referred to as a sister chromatid. The double stranded chromosome pairs become closely aligned and it is during this stage of prophase that actual physical exchanges (crossovers) can occur. During the first meiotic division, a double stranded member of each pair is contained in each of the two resulting cells. At this time, each cell contains half of the double stranded chromosome complement of the parent cell. In the second meiotic division, the sister chromatids that make up each chromosome separate into different cells. Thus, of the four resulting cells, each contains a single chromatid chromosome and one half of the total chromosome complement of the parent cell.

Numerical Aberrations

Mishaps of nature may occur and can result in somatic cells containing chromosomes different in number from the expected diploid constitution of 46. If the chromosome number is an exact multiple of the haploid number (23), it is called *polyploidy*. An example of this would be a triploidy (69,XXY or 69,XXX). These conditions are not compatible with survival. Less drastic alterations of chromosome number which are not exact multiples of the haploid number are called *aneuploidies*. Aneuploidy usually results from failure of paired chromosomes or sister chromatids to disjoin at anaphase (nondisjunction). Aneuploidy may also be due to delayed movement of a chromosome at anaphase (anaphase lag). Either of these mechanisms produces two types of cells, one with an extra copy of a chromosome and one with a missing copy of that chromosome. The reasons for meiotic nondisjunction are not known, but it occurs with increased frequency with increasing maternal age (see Figure 1–4).

Aneuploidy can arise either during meiosis or mitosis. Meiotic nondisjunction may occur at either the first or second meiotic divisions. Nondisjunction in a mitotic cell division is the mechanism by which a mosaic can arise (an individual with cell lines of two or more different chromosomal complements). The causes of mitotic nondisjunction are also ill-defined.

Down syndrome is one of the more common aneuploids observed at the time of birth. Individuals with Down syndrome (previously referred to as "mongolism") have existed since ancient times, but the condition was not described in detail until 1866. Characteristics include short stature, frequent malformations of the heart, characteristically shaped heads with distinctive facial features, and a long list of minor characteristics (many of which can be found with lower frequency in the general population). More important, individuals with Down syndrome may also be variably mentally retarded or developmentally delayed and show communication difficulties.

Individuals with Down syndrome are usually born to parents who are chromosomally normal. It was only recently (1959) that in-

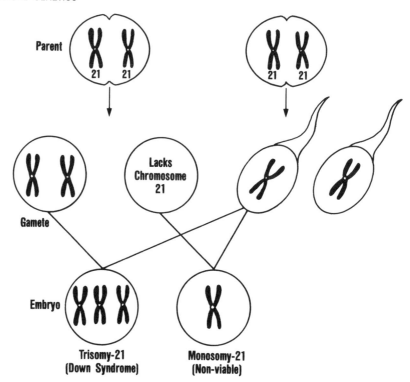

FIGURE 1–4:
Meiotic nondisjunction
leading to trisomy 21.

vestigators discovered that the somatic cells of individuals with Down syndrome contain 47 chromosomes, rather than the usual 46.

When a chromosome is present in triplicate instead of as a pair, it is referred to as a *trisomy*. Individuals trisomic for a chromosome are more prone to abnormalities of growth and development affecting both structure and function. The presence of the extra chromosome genetically "imbalances" development with major consequences, especially during the period of embryogenesis.

Structural Aberrations

Structural aberrations result from breakage of chromosomes. Generally, when breaks occur, repair mechanisms rejoin the ends, but this can lead to structural rearrangements. An increased rate of chromosome breakage has been observed in cases of ionizing radiation or mutagenic chemical exposure. There are many types of structural aberrations known, but here we will highlight only (1) translocations, and (2) deletions and duplications.

Translocations

Translocation refers to the transfer of chromosomal material from one chromosome to another. Usually, this exchange of material results in no net loss or gain of genetic information, so that individuals with this chromosomal rearrangement are phenotypically

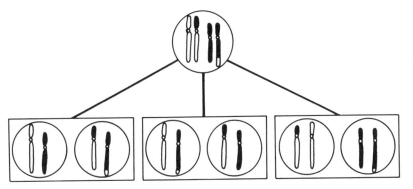

normal. Two of the more common varieties of translocations are reciprocal and centric fusion (Robertsonian).

RECIPROCAL. With reciprocal translocations, the chromosomal material between two chromosomes is exchanged. Either the long or short arm may break, and any chromosome pair may be involved.

As shown in Figure 1–5, pairing of translocation chromosomes during meiosis may not occur in an orderly fashion. Subsequently, different types of segregation can result in a variety of balanced or unbalanced gametes. Such visible imbalances involve large numbers of genes, and the affected conceptions may either be miscarried or born with multiple congenital anomalies.

CENTRIC FUSION (ROBERTSONIAN). Translocations involving centric fusion arise from breaks at or near the centromere of two acrocentric chromosomes with cross fusion of the products. This can result in a single chromosome with two centromeres (dicentric) and a fragment with no centromere (acentric). Acentric fragments are generally "lost" during cell division. One of the more common examples of centric fusion in humans involves chromosomes 14 and 21. Again, the individual that carries such a translocation is healthy, but problems may arise at the time of gametogenesis. The various types of gametes resulting from different kinds of segregation are illustrated in Figure 1–6. The gamete marked with an asterisk, if combined with a normal gamete at fertilization, would effectively result in the same phenotypic features of Down syndrome due to trisomy 21. The individual's karyotype would not demonstrate an extra chromosome, but would, in effect, have an excess of chromosome number 21 material.

Deletions and Duplications

Deletions refer to the loss of any part of a chromosome. A *duplication* is the presence of two copies of the same segment of a chromosome. These imbalances may result from chromosomal breakage, unequal crossing-over during meiosis, or from the meiotic events in a parent with a translocation or inversion. In general, deletions

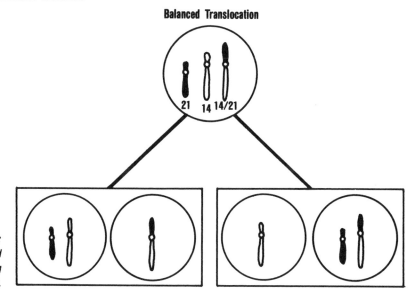

Balanced Translocation

FIGURE 1-6:
Segregation of a balanced 14/21 translocation during meiosis.

result in more serious consequences in development. Small duplications may be tolerated, but need not be entirely benign (see Figure 1-7).

The Sex Chromosome Anomalies

In 1959, it was discovered that two well-known but puzzling human afflictions, *Turner syndrome* and *Klinefelter syndrome,* were the result of sex chromosome aneuploidies. Turner syndrome is observed with a frequency of 1 per 2,500 in the female population. Individuals who have Turner syndrome are phenotypic females, but they are generally sterile because of an underdeveloped uterus and a lack of functional ovarian tissue (streak ovaries). Other features of Turner syndrome may include short stature, distinctive facial features, webbing of the neck, a broad shield-like chest, lymphedema, heart failure secondary to coarctation of the aorta, and primary amenorrhea. Individuals with Turner syndrome have a single X chromosome and are referred to in the notation 45,X or 45,XO.

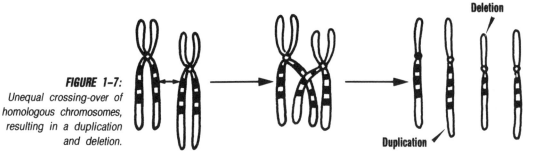

FIGURE 1-7:
Unequal crossing-over of homologous chromosomes, resulting in a duplication and deletion.

Curiously, this chromosome constitution is extremely lethal to the fetus (greater than 95 percent mortality), but if the child is born, she may be relatively healthy. Contrary to some textbook statements, individuals with Turner syndrome are not mentally retarded. Their intelligence follows the distribution seen in the normal population. In terms of treatment, an expert endocrine assessment is recommended, as one may achieve extra growth with hormone supplementation. Induction of secondary sexual characteristics may also be possible, but infertility remains a problem.

In the same year, Klinefelter syndrome was found to be associated with the sex chromosome constitution of 47,XXY. This is thought to occur approximately once in every 1,000 male births. These individuals are phenotypic males with no obvious dysmorphic traits seen at birth. Although rarely mentally retarded, many are said to have "shy" personalities. In adolescence, tall stature, delayed puberty, and gynecomastia are observed. As adults, there may be problems of infertility related to low sperm production. This may be accompanied by a diminished libido and further disturbances of behavior. Up to 20 percent of male individuals attending infertility clinics are diagnosed as having Klinefelter syndrome. Treatment with hormones during adolescence may improve behavioral characteristics and induce more normal puberty.

When to Suspect a Chromosome Disorder

In general, problems of chromosome imbalance manifest as failure to thrive and have associated multiple system problems. These may be of an obvious organic nature such as congenital heart disease, cleft lip, or microphthalmia. The clinician should be suspicious if the subject has so-called minor dysmorphic features such as low-set or malformed ears, widely spaced eyes, incurving of a finger, or a low nasal bridge. These latter findings can sometimes contribute to the general impression of a "funny looking kid."

Even in cases where a clinical diagnosis is readily apparent, such as Down syndrome, a genetic evaluation is required to confirm the cytogenetic variety, as recurrence risks will vary considerably.

In cases due to a familial 21/21 translocation, the recurrence risk is 100 percent, quite different than the one percent recurrence risk in cases due to trisomy 21! Following review of the initial results, parents or other family members may need to be studied. A family history of an excessive number of miscarriages is also an indicator for chromosome studies.

Depending on the cytogenetic services available in an area, specialized staining techniques may increase the chances of picking up the minor (small duplication or deletion syndromes) chromosome anomalies. In such cases, the advice of a geneticist should be sought.

■ Single Gene (Monogenic)

Genes are the determinants of heredity. A gene is a segment of DNA coding for a single trait, or more specifically, for a single protein or enzyme. The DNA in human cells is sufficent to account for several million genes coding for proteins of an average length of about 1,000 amino acids, yet most of this DNA is transcriptionally inactive. Probably, the number of structural-functional genes in humans is in the range of 70,000 to 100,000. Genes are not observable through conventional cytogenetic techniques.

The chromosomal site occupied by a particular gene is called a *locus*. The term *allele* refers to a gene that has one or more alternative forms. The sum total of the genetic material of a cell or of an individual is called the *genome*.

Because humans have a diploid set of chromosomes, there are two loci for each genetic determinant. The term *homozygous (homozygote)* refers to the condition of having two like alleles at a particular locus in a diploid genome. *Heterozygous (heterozygote)* refers to the condition of having two unlike alleles at a particular locus. The term *genotype* refers to an individual's genetic constitution, whereas *phenotype* is the observable expression of the genotype interacting with the environment.

In formal genetics, the term *dominant* refers to genes that produce a phenotypical effect in the heterozygous state (i.e., expressed even when present on only one chromosome of a pair). The term *recessive* applies to those traits only expressed when homozygous (i.e., when present on both chromosomes). Thus, there are basically four different patterns of inheritance, which can be classified as follows:

Autosomal Dominant

Autosomal dominant diseases appear when the patient carries a single dose of the abnormal gene (e.g., neurofibromatosis, Crouzon syndrome, Stickler syndrome). In most human autosomal dominant disorders, no homozygotes have been observed. In a few conditions in which homozygotes have been observed (achondroplasia, familial hypercholesterolemia), homozygotes are clinically much more severely affected than the heterozygotes.

Autosomal Recessive

Autosomal recessive diseases appear only when the patient carries a double dose of an abnormal gene (e.g., mucopolysaccharide storage diseases, Riley-Day syndrome, Pendred syndrome). The patient is homozygous, the parents of the patient are heterozygous in that they carry one each of the normal and abnormal allele. Usually, heterozygous parents are free of any detectable clinical manifestation.

X-Linked Recessive

X-linked recessive disorders are generally only expressed in male patients who carry the abnormal gene on their X chromosome, and in female patients who carry two abnormal genes, one on each of their two X chromosomes. In general, heterozygous female patients (who carry one abnormal gene on one X chromosome and the normal allele on the other X chromosome) do not show clinical manifestations. Examples include diseases such as classical Alport and Usher syndromes.

X-Linked Dominant

X-linked dominant disorders manifest clinically in hemizygous male patients and also in female patients who are heterozygous. An example of such a disorder is Wildervanck syndrome.

The Recognition of Monogenic Disorders

The most important factor for the clinician to consider is the possibility of a genetic disorder and to proceed with the steps required to prove or exclude this possibility. Some simple guidelines that can help in the recognition of a single gene disorder in a patient include general medical genetics knowledge and family history and pedigree analysis.

With the acquisition of general medical genetics knowledge, the health care worker learns that certain clinical entities are always caused by abnormal genes. Selected examples include Stickler syndrome, Waardenburg syndrome, and Treacher-Collins syndrome.

Family history and pedigree analysis is a very important "tool" in genetic medicine. The unit in genetic medicine is not the individual, but the family. The genetic disorder in a subject may be missed if the family history is not examined. The presence of other similarly affected members in the family makes it more likely that the disease in the patient is of genetic origin. Further evaluation is required to determine whether the disease is monogenic.

The Steps in Taking a Family History/Pedigree

When the geneticist obtains a patient's pedigree, the following information is sought:

1. Does anyone else in the family have the same disorder?

2. Does anyone else in the family have a possibly related condition?

3. Is there evidence for other genetic diseases in the family?
4. Is there anything special in the family background?

The first question may give an indication of the pattern of inheritance. A "vertical" pattern of affected persons in successive generations is characteristic of the autosomal dominant disorders. Horizontal appearance of those affected (only among the siblings of the patient) is suggestive of an autosomal recessive disorder. An appearance of the disease only in male family members related through unaffected female family members suggests that the disorder is caused by an X-linked recessive gene.

The second question relates to differences in expressivity of the genetic disorders. For example, a patient with neurofibromatosis (an autosomal dominant disorder usually characterized by neurofibroma, café-au-lait spots and neurological problems) may have all the manifestatons of neurofibromatosis, but other affected relatives may have only signs of a mild manifestation such as café-au-lait spots. This latter finding is certainly a related condition and needs to be determined in the family histories of patients with neurofibromatosis.

The third question has to do with diagnosis as well as genetic prognosis. The family history taken at the beginning of an interaction with the patient may draw attention to a particular problem for the patient. For example, a family history of deafness in several first or second degree relatives of the patient should raise the possibility that the patient may be at risk for the same disorder, indicating a need for clinical testing.

The fourth question regarding information about ethnic origin and relatedness of the patient's ancestors could also be of special importance. For example, a patient with autonomic nervous system difficulties and of Ashkenazi Jewish origin should alert the clinician to the possibility of Riley-Day syndrome. Parental consanguinity would also raise the question of whether the patient has an autosomal recessive disorder.

The technique used to extract family history information varies and much depends on prior information on the patient's condition. The symbols shown in Figure 1–8 are standardly used by geneticists in the construction of a pedigree.

Step 1

Proceed with taking a "screening pedigree" by recording and asking information about the first degree relatives of the patient (parents, siblings, offspring of the patient).

■ Draw a pedigree diagram using the symbols shown in Figure 1–8.

■ Document the status of first degree relatives of the patient. Ask and record ages, deaths and cause of death, and major illnesses for each first degree relative.

■ Ask the general question "Are there any diseases running in your family?" If the answer is positive, record this positive informa-

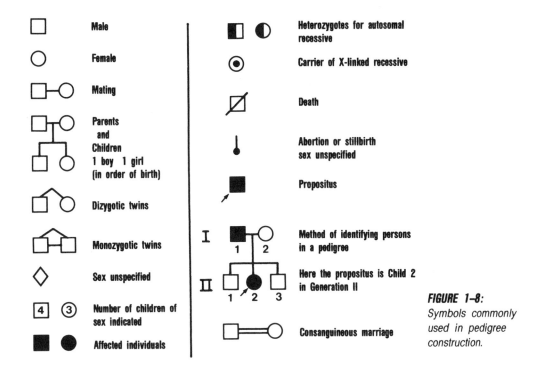

FIGURE 1–8:
Symbols commonly used in pedigree construction.

tion. Include the affected second degree relatives (aunts, uncles, grandparents, grandchildren).

■ If the patient or the parents are of child bearing age, ask whether there is any history of birth defects or mental retardation in the family background.

■ Ask the ethnic background of the patient's parents and whether they were related.

Step 2

Return to the pedigree and do a problem oriented reexamination of the family background, after the problem of the patient has been formulated and the patient's disease does not appear to be of a totally acquired nature. Ask specific questions about the presence or absence of signs, symptoms, or conditions in each one of the first degree relatives and the grandparents of the patient. If the problem appears to be familial, inquire about the presence or absence of this problem in other second degree relatives.

The taking of a careful and well-oriented pedigree:

■ helps in the documentation of the diagnosis

■ provides clues about problems the patient may have or may develop

■ is essential for providing genetic counseling to the patient

■ permits the identification and the alerting of other relatives who are at risk for developing the same disorder

Autosomal Dominant Traits

The pedigree shown in Figure 1-9 shows the typical features of autosomal dominant inheritance. Both male and female individuals are affected in approximately equal numbers. Persons are affected in each generation, and male relatives can transmit the condition to male relatives or female relatives and vice versa. Unaffected persons do not transmit the condition.

Each of the affected persons in the family shown in Figure 1-9 is a heterozygote and as each has married an unaffected person (normal homozygote), the expected ratio of affected to unaffected offspring can be predicted, as shown in Figure 1-10. It is equally likely for a child to receive the mutant or normal allele from the affected parent, so on average, there is a one-half or 50 percent chance that each child of a heterozygous parent will be affected.

So far, approximately 2,000 autosomal dominant traits have been described in humans. Some of the autosomal dominant traits are so serious that they usually preclude reproduction (e.g., Apert syndrome). In this situation, neither parent will be affected and the child will be a new mutation. If the child fails to reproduce, then the mutant gene goes no further and there will be but one affected individual in the family. There is also the suggestion that the risk for a new mutation increases with increasing paternal age.

Variation and Clinical Manifestation—Expressivity and Penetrance

In a family, persons who carry the same abnormal gene may show striking differences in clinical manifestation. Some are mildly affected, whereas others may have severe manifestations. The degree of clinical manifestation of an abnormal gene is called *expressivity.* Differences in expressivity are encountered in all the genetic disorders, but they are most prominent in the autosomal dominant disorders.

The term *penetrance* is used to denote the proportion (percentage-wise) of obligatory heterozygotes for a given autosomal

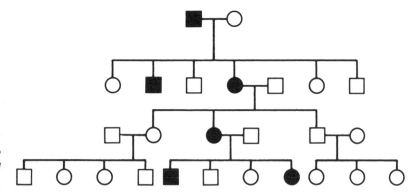

FIGURE 1-9:
Typical pedigree demonstrating autosomal dominant inheritance.

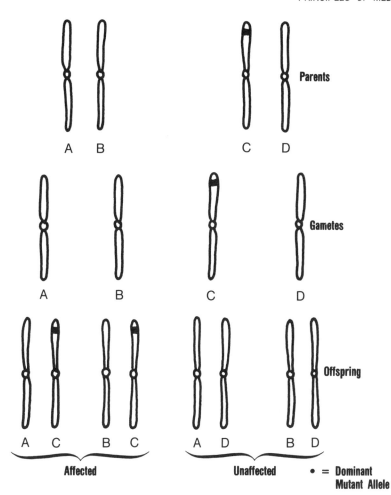

A   B   C   D   Parents

A   B   C   D   Gametes

A   C   B   C   A   D   B   D   Offspring

Affected   Unaffected   • = Dominant
                                      Mutant Allele

FIGURE 1-10:
Segregation of an
autosomal dominant
allele.

dominant gene, or of homozygotes for a given autosomal recessive gene who show any of the known phenotypic effects of the gene. Thus, 100 percent (or complete) penetrance means that all the obligatory carriers manifest with any one of the clinical phenotypical effects produced by the gene; 80 percent penetrance means that 20 percent of the obligatory heterozygotes do not manifest with any of the known clinical manifestations produced by the gene; the terms *incomplete, partial,* or *reduced* penetrance describe the absence of manifestation in an obligate gene carrier.

Penetrance is relative. A genetic disorder which today is considered to have low penetrance may become fully penetrant in the future. This is usually because of the introduction of new diagnostic methods or clinical criteria. For example, neurofibromatosis was considered to be a disorder with incomplete penetrance until recently, when research showed that a significant proportion of carriers of the neurofibromatosis gene have as their only manifestation an increased number of café-au-lait spots. When any of the clinical manifestations, including café-au-lait spots, are taken as a criterion of neurofibromatosis, penetrance is complete. When only the presence of neurofibromas is used as the clinical criteria, penetrance is reduced.

Although expressivity and penetrance are also demonstrable in autosomal recessive conditions, they are not as striking as in autosomal dominant traits.

Autosomal Recessive Traits

Suppose there is a recessive "bad" allele, coding for a defective enzyme such as is the case with the mucopolysaccharide storage diseases (e.g., Hunter syndrome). The heterozygotes with one "good" dominant and one "bad" recessive will show little or no ill effect. They will be symptomless "carriers" of the recessive allele (see Figure 1-11). At gametogenesis, one allele goes into one gamete, the other into the other.

Now, if two carriers were to have children, any child would have a 25 percent chance of being homozygous for the "good" alleles, a 2/4 (50 percent) chance of being heterozygous like the

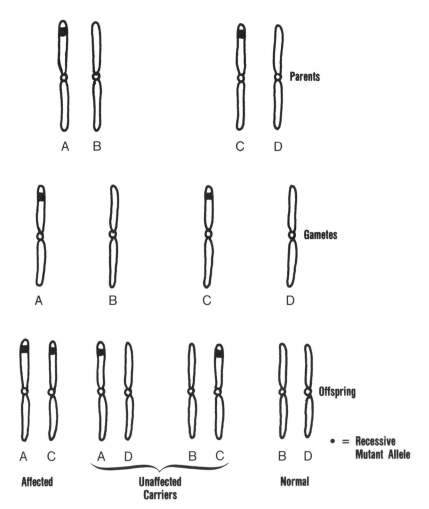

FIGURE 1-11:
Segregation of an autosomal recessive allele.

Parents

Gametes

Offspring

• = Recessive Mutant Allele

A C   A D   B C   B D

Affected   **Unaffected Carriers**   **Normal**

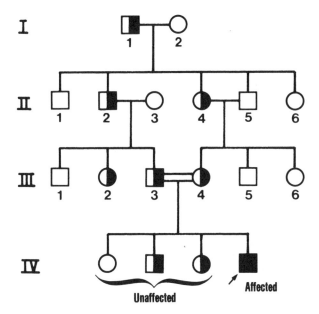

FIGURE 1-12:
An autosomal
recessive pedigree
with consanguinity
(a first cousin
marriage).

parents and a 25 percent chance for being homozygous for the "bad" allele (see Figure 1-12).

It takes two heterozygotes to make a homozygote. Each one of us probably has 5 or 6 bad recessive alleles but we will not have homozygous (and affected) children unless, by unlucky chance or consanguinity, we mate with another heterozygote for the same recessive allele.

Consanguinity

Brother-sister, father-daughter, mother-son matings (incest) have half their alleles in common. Therefore, there exists a very high risk of homozygosity. First cousin marriages (allowable in Canada, but not in all states of the United States) have 1/16 of their alleles in common. This represents an increased, but not prohibitive, risk of homozygous offspring. Some genetic considerations related to consanguinity are that (1) with very rare autosomal recessive genetic diseases consanguinity is likely; (2) where parents are related, there is the possibility of genetic disease due to homozygosity; and (3) with very many first-cousin matings, the great majority have normal children. Most geneticists do not strongly discourage cousin marriages, as the overall risk may be 6 or 7 percent compared to the general population background risk of 3 to 4 percent.

The Phenotype of the Heterozygous Carrier of a Recessive Trait

Recessive alleles are not always completely recessive, meaning that they are not always completely without expression. By special carrier detection, for some metabolic diseases such as mucopolysaccharide storage disorders, enzyme activity at a reduced, but not clinically adequate level, can be demonstrated.

Screening tests applied to a whole population for carrier testing of all heterozygosities is not possible. Although inroads are being made by selective biochemical or DNA/gene testing, the vast majority of diseases still lack this diagnostic ability. If a test were available, it could even be possible to test a fetus for homozygosity or heterozygosity of certain alleles.

Characteristics of Recessively Inherited Disorders

The following list outlines the characteristics of recessively inherited disorders:

■ The abnormal phenotype is not observed to pass from generation to generation.

■ The abnormal genotype may pass from generation to generation, but is often difficult to detect.

■ It is common to see more than one affected child in a large sibship, but in a small sibship one may only see one affected child (or, of course, none, even if both parents are heterozygous, as it is only a 25 percent risk for each child.)

■ Male and female offspring are equally affected if the allele is situated on an autosomal (not X or Y) chromosome.

■ Consanguinity increases the risk of matings of heterozygotes.

■ There can be carrier detection of some recessive alleles and screening to detect carriers in some high-risk populations.

■ Recessively inherited phenotypes can cause very serious diseases in the offspring, even though the parents appear normal phenotypically.

A prototype of an autosomal recessive trait is *Tay-Sachs disease.* This disease occurs primarily in individuals of Ashkenazi Jewish background. Frequency of the disease in Ashkenazi Jews is 1/3600 live births. The carrier frequency in Ashkenazi Jews is 1/30. This is high compared to the carrier frequency in Sephardic Jews (1/250), and in non-Jews (1/300). The clinical picture is characterized by progressive psychomotor retardation, loss of vision, the appearance of a "cherry red spot" in the macula, and the persistence of an exaggerated response to sounds. The psychomotor retardation is evident in the first year when the child demonstrates developmental delays. The child may be sullen and apathetic. The loss of vision is noted toward the latter part of the first year of life. Seizures are a later manifestation which may be difficult to control, even with medication. Death usually occurs by age 2, but a few children have lived to age 3 or 4.

Diagnosis can be established by documenting a deficiency of an enzyme (hexosaminidase-A) in serum or tissues. The enzyme deficiency leads to failure in the degradation of neuron specific chemical compounds and a subsequent accumulation and storage of these materials in neurons throughout the body. Some neurons react negatively to this substance and degenerate quite early in the course of the disease.

The disease can be diagnosed in utero by demonstration of the enzymatic defect in amniocytes, as well as at birth from enzyme assays of serum or skin fibroblasts. Heterozygote (carrier) detection is usually possible. Carriers usually demonstrate one-half the enzyme activity of homozygous normal individuals. As yet, there is no effective treatment of affected individuals except prevention through heterozygote screening programs and prenatal diagnosis.

Distinctively different from the traits or diseases determined by autosomal alleles are the genetic conditions due to X-linked genes. What follows is a simplified explanation of the basis for these differences.

X-Linked Inheritance

The female individual has two X chromosomes, one each from her father and mother. With the exception of some genes near the tip of the short arm, one of the X chromosomes is randomly inactivated in each somatic cell (i.e., *Lyonization*). This mechanism ensures that the amount of X-linked gene products produced in somatic cells of the female individual is approximately equivalent to the amount produced in male cells.

In contrast, the male individual has only one X chromosome, and hence, only one copy of each X-linked gene. The Y chromosome contains important male determinants and probably contains loci homologous to those on the tip of the short arm of the X. In the male individual, the X chromosome remains active in every cell, so *any* mutant X alleles will always be expressed. Each daughter must receive her father's X chromosome, and each son must receive his father's Y chromosome. Hence, fathers cannot transmit X-linked genes to their sons. In looking at pedigrees in which an X-linked allele is segregating, a few major characteristics can be noted, including:

■ Parents and relatives, except brothers, maternal uncles, and other male relatives of the female line, are usually unaffected.

■ Hemizygous (affected) men do not transmit the trait to children of either sex, but all their daughters are heterozygotes (carriers).

■ Heterozygous (carrier) women are almost always clinically unaffected, but transmit the trait to their sons with a segregation frequency of one-half (i.e., the probability of affected sons is 50 percent). Half of their daughters, on the average, are heterozygotes like their mothers.

■ Excluding a new germinal mutation, affected female children come only from matings of carrier (or affected) women and affected men.

■ Except for new mutants, every affected male child comes from a carrier woman (the proportion of new mutants may be high in serious or lethal conditions such as Duchenne muscular dystrophy).

The pedigree in Figure 1–12 demonstrates a family with severe X-linked muscular dystrophy and the diagram shows the expected proportions of offspring for a female individual with an X-linked recessive allele.

Duchenne Muscular Dystrophy

An example of an X-linked recessive inheritance is Duchenne muscular dystrophy. This condition produces a progressive proximal muscle weakness with massive elevation of all muscle enzymes, including creatine phosphokinase (CPK). The onset is in early childhood and most children are wheelchair bound by 10 years of age. There is a marked discrepancy of the sex ratio, with primarily boys affected. Heterozygous females are clinically unaffected (carriers) but may transmit the condition to the next generation. The condition is never transmitted by an unaffected man.

As previously stated, the female carrier is usually clinically normal. However, because of Lyonization, a proportion of her muscle cells will have the active X, which carries the mutant allele. These cells will release CPK, so that in about two-thirds of female carriers, the CPK lies outside the normal range. This is helpful in carrier detection, provided precautions are taken to exclude other factors that can raise (exercise, intramuscular injections) or lower (pregnancy) this enzyme level. A woman with an affected child and an affected brother or a woman with more than one affected child is considered an obligate carrier, as the alternative explanation of multiple new mutations is so unlikely. For each daughter of an obligate carrier there is a one-half risk that she too is a carrier.

CPK testing may help to resolve this. More recently, carrier detection using tests based on recombinant DNA technology has been possible. Further work in this area will be directed at determining what protein is affected by the mutation. Only then will there be hope of understanding the basic pathophysiological process. This may eventually lead to more effective management or treatment strategies (see Figure 1–13).

■ Polygenic-Multifactorial

In Mendelian (or monogenic) diseases, and in the chromosomal malformations, genetic factors are clearly implicated. In many Mendelian diseases, the unifactorial defect can be demonstrated

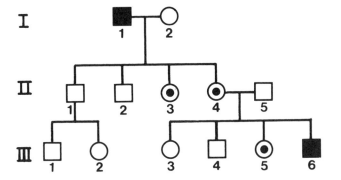

FIGURE 1-13:
Typical pedigree of an X-linked recessive disorder such as Duchenne muscular dystrophy.

biochemically as a protein or enzyme defect. Most of the advances in medical genetics so far have been made by studies on these types of disease using biochemical, immunological, and cytological methods. However, there are many common diseases (arbitrarily defined as having a frequency of more than 1/1000) in which a simple etiology usually cannot be demonstrated. The family pedigree pattern does not allow a diagnosis of monogenic inheritance, but there is a definite familial tendency, the proportion of affected relatives being greater than in the general population. The proportion of affected relatives is often only of the order of five percent or less (much less than would be expected on a simple unifactorial basis). The most likely explanation is that these disorders are inherited on a polygenic-multifactorial basis. This implies that the cause is partly environmental and partly due to the effects of many genes, each of small effect.

Syndromes contained in this book following this pattern of inheritance include isolated cleft lip or palate, Pierre-Robin syndrome, and stuttering.

How do we know that genetic factors are operative in these diseases or traits? We still need to depend upon family history data (or population studies) for the implication of polygenic-multifactorial factors in disease etiology. Evidence suggesting the operation of genetic factors in a disease includes:

■ Familial aggregation (but beware of familial aggregation due solely to environmental reasons)

■ Monozygous (MZ) twins, who are more frequently affected than dizygous (DZ) twins

■ MZ twins reared apart who have greater concordance (i.e., both affected) for the disease or trait than expected by chance

■ Adopted children who resemble their biological parents rather than their adoptive parents in disease frequency

■ Biological relatives who have increased disease frequency but spouses who do not, even though living in the same environment

A number of models have been proposed for multifactorial inheritance, but the one most widely used is referred to as the "threshold model." In the threshold model, it is assumed that there are multiple genes or environmental factors which, when the balance exceeds a certain threshold, cause a certain malformation or problem to occur. The further the threshold is exceeded, the greater the extent of the malformation.

The more severe the malformation or trait, the more the parents' liability and the higher the incidence in relatives. Thus, approximately five percent of first degree relatives are affected. This five percent figure is a commonly quoted one for recurrence risks in first degree relatives of the affected individual. Some polygenic-multifactorial traits show a marked sex predilection (e.g., in cleft lip or cleft palate).

There are several practical consequences of a threshold model. If the disorder in question is inherited on a multifactorial basis, one could predict:

■ A sharp decline in frequency from first degree to second degree to third degree relatives. Usually, the only significant recurrence risk is for first degree relatives. Other relatives have a risk similar to that found in the general population.

■ The more severe the malformation or characteristic, the higher the frequency will be among the close relatives (presumably because there are more liability factors within that family).

■ The more affected relatives, the higher the risk to others, presumably because this indicates that there are more abnormal genes segregating in the family, or the family has been more exposed to a precipitating environmental factor(s).

■ When there is a sex difference in the population frequency, the frequency among relatives of an affected individual of the less frequently affected sex will be _greater_ than the frequency among relatives of affected individuals of the more frequently affected sex. This is presumably because individuals of the less frequently affected sex have a higher threshold, so will have greater number of high risk liability factors in order to have had that trait. Thus, the risk to their relatives will be correspondingly higher.

■ Environmental-Genetic Interactions Influencing Development of the Embryo or Fetus

Teratogens

A _teratogen_ is defined as a drug or any other environmental agent that causes abnormal development of an organism. As public awareness regarding teratogens as a possible cause of birth defects increases, the question as to what is "safe" during a pregnancy will become increasingly common. Awareness of known teratogens is often invaluable in prevention of serious fetal damage. It is important to be able to identify teratogens as a cause of birth defects, as many teratogenic agents can be eliminated from a future pregnancy. Examples of this group include:

- physical agents (e.g., radiation)
- infectious agents (e.g., rubella)
- maternal conditions (e.g., diabetes)
- maternal diet/drugs (e.g., alcohol)
- uterine factors (e.g., amniotic bands)

It is important for the physician to be able to identify teratogens as a cause of birth defects, as many teratogenic agents can be eliminated from a future pregnancy. The most common examples of this group include drugs ingested by the mother, the classic example being Thalidomide.

Important Considerations in Teratology

FETAL SUSCEPTIBILITY. The time period of susceptibility-vulnerability is usually very specific. Exposure during the first trimester of pregnancy is probably the most harmful, correlating with the most sensitive period of organogenesis.

DOSE RELATIONSHIP. The "dose" of the teratogen is important. Many cases of teratogen exposures are minimal (e.g., a chest x-ray during pregnancy) and the patient may be counseled regarding the low risk of harmful effects, but situations will arise where the answer may not be as clear cut. Here, consultation may be helpful.

HEREDITARY PREDISPOSITION. This refers to the differences in which individuals (both mothers and fetuses) react to, or handle, exposure to teratogenic substances. At present, it is virtually impossible to predict which individuals may be more susceptible because of their genetic makeup.

Some newer findings related to teratogenesis include:

- The teratogen may cause different malformations at different times in gestation.
- Teratogens may produce several different patterns of malformations.
- Teratogens may increase "background" malformations, as well as producing a specific syndrome, (e.g., anticonvulsants and the possibility of cleft lip or cleft palate).
- In addition to altered morphogenesis, teratogens may result in less obvious clinical problems (i.e., prenatal onset of growth delay, infertility or wastage, altered central nervous system [CNS] performance, carcinogenic potential).
- The age at which abnormalities become obvious may vary or may be long after birth.

With regard to avoidance of known or possible teratogens, physicians and patients often face decisions based upon their perceptions of benefits versus possible harmful effects. This is particularly true with prescription drugs (e.g., antiepileptic drugs like Dilantin) and habits of lifestyle (e.g., cigarette smoking and alcohol consumption). Nothing can be considered absolutely safe during pregnancy. Directions for patient management must be based on the most current information from the growing body of knowledge in teratology.

■ Summary

Understanding the genetic factors involved in disease processes allows us to more fully appreciate the reasons for the extreme variability between individuals. A disease needs to be viewed against the background of genetic variation and the influence of environmental factors.

The following chapters delineate some of the major genetic syndromes that have communicative disorders associated with them. Readers will be challenged to use their knowledge regarding variability in disease expression in a clinically meaningful way. Arriving at an earlier definitive diagnosis may be possible by being sensitive toward variability in syndrome features or time of onset. Awareness of genetic factors and modes of inheritance might also help in earlier detection of other family members at risk for a condition. Our goal is that patients or clients should benefit from these anticipated improvements in diagnosis, management, and preventative strategies.

Chapter 2

Chromosomal Syndromes

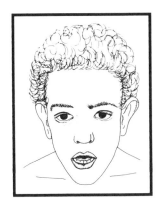

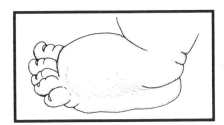

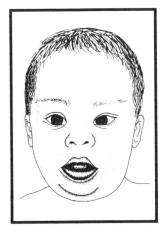

Down Syndrome ■
(Trisomy 21)

Fragile X Syndrome ■

Turner Syndrome ■
(XO Syndrome)

Down Syndrome
(Trisomy 21)

■ Characteristics
Dysmorphology

Down syndrome is one of the most common chromosomal abnormalities, with an estimated incidence of one in every 700 live births (de Grouchy & Truleau, 1984). The diagnosis can be made clinically on the basis of characteristics that may include (see list):

generalized hypotonia

hyperextensible joints

brachycephaly

flat facial profile

upslanting palpebral fissures

epicanthal folds

speckling of iris (Brushfield spots)

small nose

tendency toward protrusion of tongue

small anomalous auricles

excess skin on back of neck

cardiac malformations (in approximately 40 percent)

duodenal atresia

developmental delay or mental retardation

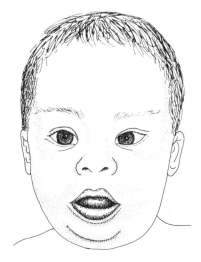

Typical Down syndrome facies. The eyes demonstrate the epicanthal folds. The tongue is relatively large with a tendency to protrude. This is accentuated by a small chin.

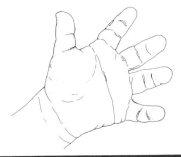

Relatively short fingers and altered palmar creases. Here, a classic transverse palmar crease (Simian crease) is demonstrated. There is also mild incurving of the fifth finger (clinodactyly) secondary to dysplasia of the fifth middle finger bone.

Epicanthal fold and Brushfield spots of iris.

The previously mentioned features are not specific for Down syndrome as they may be found with variable frequency in the general population. However, the clustering of features is what allows for clinical suspicion and diagnosis. There exist many excellent reviews of other signs or symptoms (Gorlin & Pindborg, 1964; Smith, 1982). Recent research has included development of a scoring system based on objective criteria to aid in the clinical diagnosis (Rex & Preus, 1982), molecular genetics studies (Smith, 1985), and the predisposition of Down syndrome individuals to Alzheimer disease (Heston, 1977).

Hearing

One of the most consistent physical abnormalities associated with Down syndrome is small auricles. Aase, Wilson, and Smith (1973) reported that 84 percent of babies with Down syndrome had ears that fell below the third percentile for length of ears. Other physical anomalies related to the outer ear include: overfolding of upper helix of the pinna, small or absent earlobes, and stenosis of the external ear canal (Balkany, 1980; Pueschel, 1978; Sando, Suehiro, & Wood, 1983).

Hearing loss is very common among individuals with Down syndrome. It is estimated that more than 75 percent of all children with Down syndrome have either unilateral or bilateral hearing impairment (Balkany, Downs, Jafek, & Krajicek, 1979; Brooks, Wooley, & Kanjilal, 1972; Dahle & McCollister, 1986; Hartley, 1986; Keiser, Montague, Wold, Maure, & Pattison, 1981; Libb, Dahle, Smith, McCollister, & McLain, 1985; Van Gorp & Baker, 1984). Conductive hearing disorders are the most prevalent and according to Balkany and colleagues (1979), may be present in 83 percent of cases. Sensorineural hearing loss is noted in approximately 10 to 15 percent and mixed type hearing loss in eight percent of all children with Down syndrome who display some type of hearing impairment.

Typically, conductive hearing loss among individuals with Down syndrome varies in severity from mild (i.e., greater than 15 dB HL) to moderate (i.e., approximately 50 dB HL). Studies have reported that impacted cerumen was the most frequently occurring problem among children with Down syndrome (Balkany et al., 1979; Dahle & McCollister, 1986; Schwartz & Schwartz, 1978). Other otologic problems related to the outer or the middle ear include retracted tympanic membrane and middle ear effusion (Balkany et al., 1979; Brooks et al., 1972; Dahle & McCollister, 1986). It is hypothesized that susceptibility to infections of the upper respiratory tract along with congenital malformations of the nasopharynx and Eustachian tube may be the underlying causes for the high incidence of middle ear effusion observed among children with this syndrome (Brooks et al., 1972; McIntire, Menolascino, & Wiley, 1965; Northern & Downs, 1984). Northern and Downs (1984) stated that congenital ossicular malformations or destructions of the ossicles caused by chronic middle ear infection are also causes for some conductive hearing loss observed among such children.

Otoadmittance audiometry has been reported to be an effective evaluation procedure to assess and monitor middle ear function among individuals with Down syndrome (Brooks et al., 1972; Dahle & McCollister, 1986; Libb et al., 1985; Northern (1980); Northern & Downs, 1984). Balkany and colleagues (1979) reported that 76 percent of children with the syndrome displayed abnormal tympanograms (i.e., types B, C, or A_s, according to Jerger, 1970).

Sensorineural hearing loss is more common among individuals with Down syndrome than among control groups of peers (Brooks et al., 1972; Keiser et al., 1981). The degree of sensorineural hearing loss may vary considerably. However, there appears to be a predominance of hearing loss in the range from mild to moderately severe. Moreover, bilateral are more common than monaural sensorineural hearing losses among such individuals (Brooks et al., 1972).

Brain stem evoked response audiometry (BSER) may be a useful diagnostic procedure for young children or older individuals with Down syndrome who do not cooperate when conventional audiometric procedures are used. The applicability of BSER to the Down syndrome population as well as the information revealed by BSER from individuals with Down syndrome are not clearly established (Young, 1985). Some studies have observed abnormal BSER (Folsom, Widen, & Wilson, 1983; Squires, Buchwald, Liley, & Strecker, 1982). Others have found that once corrections for conductive hearing loss are taken into account, the BSER patterns of individuals with Down syndrome are comparable to those of nondisabled controls (Maurizi, Ottaviani, Paludetti, & Lungarotti, 1985).

Finally, there is a significant incidence of hearing loss among adults with Down syndrome. Keiser and colleagues (1981) reported an incidence of 39 percent of middle ear dysfunctions among adults and twice that proportion of individuals with a sensorineural or a mixed (sensorineural and conductive) hearing loss. The incidence of a sensorineural hearing loss (or a sensorineural component in the hearing loss) increases as a function of the age of such individuals (Brooks et al., 1972; Keiser et al., 1981). No specific audiometric configuration emerged from the subjects they tested. The probability of developing a sensorineural hearing loss is much higher among adults with Down syndrome than in the population at large. These findings suggest that individuals with this syndrome may exhibit an acquired rather than a congenital hearing loss. The sensorineural component of hearing loss observed among some individuals with Down syndrome may be the result of long-standing middle ear disease (Brooks et al., 1972; Keiser et al., 1981).

Speech

Oral manifestations of the disorder include midface dysplasia with relative prognathism, open bite, posterior cross bite, enlarged tongue with fissuring and irregularities, relatively small oral opening, dry, fissured lip structure, delayed eruption of teeth, and missing teeth. The primary palate is often narrow and high arched, and submucous clefts of the uvula and portions of the secondary palate may occur more often among children with Down syndrome. The short neck structure is also associated with a more cephalic placed larynx and the shortened oral pharyngeal structures are associated with nasal airway breathing difficulties (Gorlin & Pindborg, 1964; Vigild, 1985).

Of the manifestations of the syndrome, the cognitive developmental handicap appears to be the most deleterious to speech and language acquisition and usage. It has been suggested that 50 to 60 percent of the population has IQ scores in the range between 30 and 50 (Kirk & Gallagher, 1979). Stoel-Gammon (1981) has noted that infants with Down syndrome demonstrate preverbal vocalizations not unlike children who are nondisabled, but have onset and development of meaningful speech approximately seven months behind such children. In addition, these children are slower in their development of language, including aspects of morphology (Lovell & Bradbury, 1967; Newfield & Schlanger, 1968), syntax (Lackner, 1968), semantics (Coggins, 1979), and comprehension (Lovell & Dixon, 1967).

Studies of articulatory (phonological) development after the onset of meaningful speech suggest that children with Down syndrome have a slower rate of development than children who are nondisabled and that they make more inconsistent errors than other retarded or nondisabled children (Stoel-Gammon, 1980). Further, some develop phonological processes that differ dramatically from those of children who are nondisabled.

Vocal quality disturbances emanate from both laryngeal and velopharyngeal levels. In general, individuals with Down syndrome appear to have more breathy, husky, and perceptually lower pitched and more acoustically variable voices than do individuals who are nondisabled (Montague & Hollien, 1973; Moran & Gilbert, 1982; Pentz & Gilbert, 1983). In addition, hypernasality and nasal air emission appear to be common (Kline & Hutchinson, 1980; Massengill, 1972; Rolfe, Montague, Tirman, & Vandergrift, 1979). Some of the hypernasality present may be due to poor motor control that affects the timing of velopharyngeal closure rather than an overt cleft or submucous cleft of the secondary palate. Further, problems of voice quality may be the result of faulty interaction between the laryngeal and velopharyngeal subsystems that are further distorted by a short, often excessively mucous lined, oral pharyngeal cavity.

The extent of linguistic deviance appears to mirror cognitive level and the number of associated features of the syndrome that are present. Individuals with Down syndrome generally show a slower development of all language and articulatory skills, with some individuals showing large lags, and others having skills within the lower end of normal (Stoel-Gammon, 1981). In addition, some individuals have relatively normal, whereas others have severely abnormal, voice quality (Pentz & Gilbert, 1983).

Management

Genetics and Medical

Down syndrome is due to relative excess of all or part of chromosome 21. The most common variety is due to an extra whole number 21 chromosome (trisomy 21). This accounts for 95 percent of all cases. The other two varieties, due to chromosomal translocation or mosaicism, will not be discussed in detail here. However, it is important to perform chromosome tests on all individuals with clinical Down syndrome to accurately determine the type, as genetic implications will vary greatly.

A woman of any child-bearing age may have a child with trisomy 21, but there is the well-described relationship to maternal age. Compared to the general population incidence of approximately 1 in 700, the risk at 35 years is 1 in 350; 37 years, 1 in 200; 40 years, 1 in 100; and 45 years, 1 in 25 (Thompson & Thompson, 1986).

After the birth of a child with trisomy 21, the couple has an increased risk for a chromosome abnormality in any subsequent pregnancy. The recurrence risk is estimated at 1 in 200 for Down syndrome specifically, or 1 in 100 for any chromosome abnormality. Prenatal diagnosis utilizing either amniocentesis or chorionic villi sampling should be options discussed in further management.

If malformations of the gastrointestinal system (duodenal atresia) or heart are present, they will require prompt medical and/or surgical management. Recurrent respiratory tract infections are also said to be problematic in early childhood. Adults with Down syndrome are also at greater risk for early Alzheimer disease and a variety of affective disorders. Infant stimulation programs can often help in optimizing general development.

Hearing

The deleterious effects of minimal hearing loss on language and educational achievement is well documented (Menyuk, 1977). The majority of children with Down syndrome will suffer from a hearing impairment. Thus, it is important that programs to monitor hearing disorders be designed and accessible to children with Down syndrome. Downs (1980) has recommended that such children younger than 8 years of age should undergo an otological examination and audiological evaluation at least every six months. Yearly consultation should be provided for older children and adults. Whenever indicated, appropriate audiological and otological treatment and management should be provided (Keiser et al., 1981). Hearing aids should be considered when a sensorineural hearing loss (or component) is present or if the conductive hearing loss persists. Parents, caretakers, and educators should be informed of the cause, treatment, and management of hearing losses that accompany Down syndrome (Cunningham & McArthur, 1981).

Speech

Early intervention for speech and language development is typically recommended once the syndrome has been documented. In general, early intervention in all areas of language development has been shown to aid the child with Down syndrome in attaining better cognitive strategies and processes. Many of the problems that are identified center around the inability to comprehend instructions, plan alternative courses of action, attend to one task, and express needs in a competent fashion to cope linguistically with environmental demands (Hartley, 1986; Sparks, 1984). With increasing age and the onset in some patients of dementia, gains found through direct management will be lost and associated physical, cognitive, linguistic, and psychosocial difficulties will prevail.

Surgical and dental management of oral-facial defects will follow traditional paths for closure of palatal clefts and care of dental anomalies. Recently, surgical operations have been offered to reduce tongue size or reconfigure facial features to offer a more cosmetically pleasing appearance (Parsons, Iacono, & Rozner, 1987). Changes in tongue size have not altered basic linguistic or phonological features of language or speech production.

Prognosis

The presence or absence of medical problems such as serious congenital heart disease will often be a major determinant of health and life span. Progress in surgery has improved survival in cases with life threatening malformations. The relationship of this syndrome to Alzheimer disease needs further study.

Many gains may be expected in the speech and language areas if proper identification of the linguistic needs are made early and follow-up is maintained. Improvement of voice quality may also result from therapy, providing the individual has the cognitive awareness and compliance to accept the therapy program.

Long-term studies concerning the effectiveness of infant stimulation programs are not yet available. The range of severity is wide enough in individuals with Down syndrome that some are capable of an independent adult lifestyle.

■ References

Aase, J. M., Wilson, A. C., & Smith, D. W. (1973). Small ears in Down's syndrome: A helpful diagnostic aid. *Journal of Pediatrics, 82,* 845–847.

Balkany, T. J. (1980). Otologic aspects of Down's syndrome. *Seminars in Speech, Language and Hearing, 1,* 39–48.

Balkany, T., Downs, M., Jafek, B., & Krajicek, M. (1979). Hearing loss in Down's syndrome. *Clinical Pediatrics, 18,* 116–118.

Brooks, D. N., Wooley, Hl, & Kanjilal, G. C. (1972). Hearing loss and middle ear disorders in patients with Down's syndrome (Mongolism). *Journal of Mental Deficiency Research, 16,* 21–28.

Coggins, T. (1979). Relational meaning encoded in two-word utterances of stage I Down's syndrome children. *Journal of Speech and Hearing Research, 22,* 166–178.

Cunningham, C., & McArthur, K. (1981). Hearing loss and treatment in young Down's syndrome children. *Child: Care, Health and Development, 7,* 357–374.

Dahle, A. J., & McCollister, F. P. (1986). Hearing and otologic disorders in children with Down syndrome. *American Journal of Mental Deficiency, 90,* 636–642.

de Grouchy, J., & Turleau, C. (1984). 21 trisomy. *Clinical Atlas of Human Chromosomes* (pp. 338). New York: John Wiley & Sons.

Downs, M. P. (1980). The hearing of Down's individuals. *Seminars in Speech, Language and Hearing, 1,* 25–38.

Folsom, R. C., Widen, J. E., & Wilson, W. R. (1983). Auditory brainstem responses in infants with Down's syndrome. *Archives of Otolaryngology, 109,* 607–610.

Gorlin, R., & Pindborg, J. (1964). *Syndromes of the head and neck.* New York: McGraw-Hill.

Hartley, X. Y. (1986). A summary of recent research into the development of children with Down's syndrome. *Journal of Mental Deficiency Research, 30,* 1–14.

Heston, L. L. (1977). Alzheimer's disease, trisomy 21 and myeloproliferative disorders: Associations suggesting a genetic diathesis. *Science, 196,* 322–323.

Jerger, J. (1970). Clinical experience with impedance audiometry. *Archives of Otolaryngology, 92,* 311–324.

Keiser, H., Montague, J., Wold, D., Maune, S., & Pattison, D. (1981). Hearing loss of Down syndrome adults. *American Journal of Mental Deficiency, 85,* 467–472.

Kirk, S., & Gallagher, J. (1979). *Educating exceptional children.* Boston: Houghton Mifflin.

Kline, L. S., & Hutchinson, J. M. (1980). Acoustic and perceptual evaluation of hypernasality of mentally retarded persons. *American Journal of Mental Deficiency, 85,* 153–160.

Lackner, J. R. (1968). A developmental study of language behavior in retarded children. *Neuropsychologia, 6,* 301–320.

Libb, J. W., Dahle, A., Smith, K., McCollister, F. P., & McLain, C. (1985). Hearing disorder and cognitive function of individuals with Down syndrome. *American Journal of Mental Deficiency, 90,* 353–356.

Lovell, K., & Bradbury, B. (1967). The learning of English morphology in educationally subnormal special school children. *American Journal of Mental Deficiency, 71,* 609–615.

Lovell, K., & Dixon, E. (1967). The growth of the control of grammar in imitation, comprehension, and production. *Journal of Child Psychology and Psychiatry, 8,* 31–39.

Massengill, R. (1972). *Hypernasality: Considerations in causes and treatment procedures.* Springfield, IL: C. C. Thomas.

Maurizi, M., Ottaviani, F., Paludetti, G., & Lungarotti, S. (1985). Audiological findings in Down's children. *International Journal of Pediatric Otorhinolaryngology, 9,* 227–232.

McIntire, M. S., Menolascino, F. J., & Wiley, J. H. (1965). Mongolism: Some clinical aspects. *American Journal of Mental Deficiency, 69,* 794–800.

Menyuk, P. (1977). Effects of hearing loss on language acquisition in the babbling stage. In B. Jaffe (Ed.), *Hearing disorders in children* (pp. 621–629). Baltimore: University Park Press.

Montague, J. C., & Hollien, H. (1973). Perceived voice quality disorders in Down's syndrome children. *Journal of Communication Disorders, 6,* 76–87.

Moran, M. J., & Gilbert, H. (1982). Selected acoustic characteristics and listener judgments of the voice of Down's syndrome adults. *American Journal of Mental Deficiency, 86,* 553–556.

Newfield, M., & Schlanger, B. (1968). The acquisition of English morphology by normal and educable mentally retarded children. *Journal of Speech and Hearing Research, 11,* 693–706.

Northern, J. L. (1980). Acoustic impedance measures in the Down's population. *Seminars in Speech, Language and Hearing, 1,* 81–86.

Northern, J. L., & Downs, M. P. (1984). *Hearing in children* (3rd ed.). Baltimore: Williams & Wilkins.

Parsons, C. L., Iacono, T., & Rozner, L. (1987). Effect of tongue reduction on articulation in children with Down's syndrome. *American Journal of Mental Deficiency, 91,* 328–332.

Pentz, A., & Gilbert, H. (1983). Relation of selected acoustical parameters and perceptual ratings to voice quality of Down's syndrome children. *American Journal of Mental Deficiency, 88,* 203–210.

Pueschel, S. M. (Ed.). (1978). *Down syndrome: Growing and learning.* Kansas City: Andrews & McMeel.

Rex, A. P., & Preus, M. (1982). A diagnostic index for Down syndrome. *Journal of Pediatrics, 100,* 903–906.

Rolfe, C. R., Montague, J. C., Tirman, R. M., & Vandergrift, J. F. (1979). Pilot perceptual and physiological investigation of hypernasality in Down's syndrome adults. *Folia Phoniatrica, 31,* 177–187.

Sando, I., Suehiro, S., & Wood, R. P., II. (1983). Congenital anomalies of the external and middle ear. In C. D. Bluestone & S. E. Stool (Eds.), *Pediatric otolaryngology, 1* (pp. 315). Philadelphia: W. B. Saunders.

Schwartz, D. M., & Schwartz, R. M. (1978). Acoustic impedance and otoscopic findings in young children with Down's syndrome. *Archives of Otolaryngology, 104,* 652–656.

Smith, D. W. (1982). *Recognizable patterns of human malformation* (3rd ed.). Philadelphia: W. B. Saunders.

Smith, G. F. (Ed.). (1985). Molecular structure of the number 21 chromosome and Down syndrome. *Annals of the New York Academy of Sciences, 450.*

Sparks, S. (1984). *Birth defects and speech and language disorders.* San Diego: College-Hill Press.

Squires, N., Buchwald, J., Liley, F., & Strecker, J. (1982). Brainstem auditory evoked potential abnormalities in retarded adults. In J. Courjon, F. Mauguiere, & M. Revol (Eds.), *Clinical applications of evoked potentials in neurology.* New York: Raven Press.

Stoel-Gammon, C. (1980). Phonological analysis of four Down's syndrome children. *Applied Psycholinguistics, 1,* 31–48.

Stoel-Gammon, C. (1981). Speech development of infants and children with Down syndrome. In J. K. Darby (Ed.), *Speech evaluation in medicine* (pp. 341–360). New York: Grune & Stratton, Inc.

Thompson, J. S., & Thompson, M. W. (1986). *Genetics in medicine.* Toronto: W. B. Saunders.

Van Gorp, E., & Baker, R. (1984). The incidence of hearing impairment in a sample of Down's syndrome school children. *International Journal of Rehabilitation Research, 7,* 198–200.

Vigild, M. (1985). Prevalence of malocclusion in mentally retarded young adults. *Community Dentistry and Oral Epidemiology, 13,* 183–184.

Young, C. V. (1985). Developmental disabilities. In J. Katz (Ed.), *Handbook of clinical audiology* (3rd ed.) (pp. 689–706). Baltimore: Williams & Wilkins.

Fragile X Syndrome

■ Characteristics
Dysmorphology

Recent delineation of fragile X syndrome represents a significant advance in our undertanding of mental retardation. It is second only to Down syndrome as a genetic cause of mental retardation (Turner et al., 1986). Persons with fragile X syndrome are said to have distinctive personalities, with shyness and friendliness being common attributes. The clinical phenotype includes (see list):

mental retardation

large ears

prominent jaw

macroorchidism

autism

delayed motor and speech development

Large ears, prominent jaw, and the generally long face commonly seen in the fragile X syndrome.

Hearing

Abnormal auricles are commonly associated with fragile X syndrome. Typical description of the ears of individuals with fragile X syndrome include poorly formed (sometimes bat-like) ears (De Arce & Kearnes, 1984; Gillberg, Pearsson, & Wahlstrom, 1985; Turner, Brookwell, Daniel, Selikowitz, & Zilibowitz, 1980) and simple and large ears measuring up to two standard deviations above the mean (Rogers & Simenson, 1987). There is no evidence that deviant anatomical structure of the pinna would cause or accompany a hearing loss.

Conductive or sensorineural hearing loss is rarely, if ever, associated with the fragile X syndrome. One study (Howard-Peebles, Stoddard, & Mims, 1979) reported that subjects with the fragile X syndrome performed poorly in the areas of auditory reception and auditory sequential memory on the Illinois Test of Psycholinguistic Abilities (ITPA). However, other investigations have, so far, failed to replicate these findings (Herbst, Dunn, Dill, Kalousek, & Krywaniuk, 1981).

Speech

The speech characteristics associated with this syndrome have been described as "perseverative," having a characteristic "litany-like" intonation, "jocose," "limited," and "defective" (Paul, Cohen, Breg, Watson & Herman, 1984). Howard-Peebles and colleagues (1979) reported that these individuals have more strengths in nonverbal than verbal skills, and articulation errors similar to those seen in Down syndrome and in nonimpaired children during the developmental period. They concluded that their study sample showed a generalized language disability. Hanson, Jackson, and Hagerman (1986) concluded that receptive vocabulary skills were relatively strong compared to weak auditory receptive memory and processing skills.

In a comprehensive study of the speech and language characteristics of individuals with fragile X syndrome, Wolf-Schein and colleagues (1987) compared 35 male subjects with fragile X syndrome to 15 male subjects with Down syndrome. Their data were interpreted to demonstrate that the specific language deviances shown by the subjects with fragile X syndrome could not be attributable to level of mental retardation. The subjects with fragile X syndrome were found to demonstrate more jargon, perseveration, and echolalia. The linguistic behavior of the male individual with fragile X syndrome is more inappropriate, and he talks to himself more. Further, the individual with fragile X syndrome does not tend to use nonverbal behaviors to aid his communication. Hence, he is perceived as having more autistic-like behaviors than the speaker with Down syndrome.

Range of severity relates primarily to the degree of mental retardation seen in association with this syndrome. As stated earlier, patients may show normal intelligence, or profound mental retardation. However, the majority of patients are moderately to severely mentally retarded.

Management

Genetics and Medical

The fragile X syndrome is characterized genetically by the occurrence of a fragile site on the long arm of the X chromosome at Xq27 (Rogers & Simensen, 1987) (see Figure 2-1). This hereditary fragile site requires specialized cytogenetic techniques to demonstrate it. The cytogenetic diagnosis has only recently been possible, so older techniques of chromosome study cannot be used to exclude this diagnosis. It should be suspected especially in families with numerous affected male members. Although heterozygous female carriers are generally not affected, one-third may possibly exhibit mild retardation or a learning disability (Jacobs et al., 1980; Turner et al., 1980). Demonstration of the fragile site in female carriers becomes more difficult with increasing age, so testing should be done at an early age. Not all forms of X-linked mental retardation are associated with the fragile site, some being termed nonspecific X-linked mental retardation. It is expected that advances in molecular genetics studies will further our understanding of this group of diseases. At present, prenatal diagnosis is available in some families by the application of restricion fragment length polymorphism linkage studies.

Although the results remain controversial, folic acid therapy has been used with apparent success by Rogers and Simensen (1987), who noted an improvement in intellect and behavior. These patients demonstrated longer attention span, decreased hyperactivity, as well as other behavioral improvements. Long-term studies are needed to clarify this issue in management.

Speech

There are no reports regarding the success of behavioral therapy directed toward speech and language development in this population. Given that mental retardation of some degree is typically involved, special education personnel working in concert with speech and language therapists may be expected to optimize the communication capacities of these patients. More mildly affected individuals may be expected to enjoy some success in integrated educational settings, with appropriate following and remedial assistance.

FIGURE 2-1:
The X chromosome, with the arrow pointing at the fragile site.

Prognosis

Prognosis will depend largely on the severity of intellectual impairment. Those who are mildly impaired might reasonably be expected to benefit from educational and speech and language intervention. On the other hand, those with severe mental retardation may be expected to experience more difficulty in their communicative attempts and integration into society, even with educational and speech and language intervention. More novel therapies, such as folic acid supplementation, still need further investigation.

■ References

De Arce, M. A., & Kearns, A. (1984). The fragile X syndrome: The patients and their chromosomes. *Journal of Medical Genetics, 21,* 84–91.

Gillberg, C., Pearsson, E., & Wahlstrom, J. (1985). The autism-fragile-X syndrome (AFRZY): A population-based study of ten boys. *Journal of Mental Deficiency Research, 30,* 27–39.

Hanson, D., Jackson, A., & Hagerman, R. (1986). Speech disturbances (cluttering) in mildly impaired males with the Martin Bell/fragile X syndrome. *American Journal of Medical Genetics, 23,* 195–206.

Herbst, D. S., Dunn, H. C., Dill, F. J., Kalousek, D. K., & Krywaniuk, L. W. (1981). Further delineation of X-linked mental retardation. *Human Genetics, 58,* 366–372.

Howard-Peebles, P., Stoddard, G., & Mims, M. (1979). Familial linked mental retardation, verbal disability, and marker X chromosomes. *American Journal of Human Genetics, 31,* 214–222.

Jacobs, P. A., Glover, T. W., Mayer, M., Fox, P., Gerrard, J. W., Dunn, H. G., & Herbst, D. S. (1980). X-linked mental retardation: A study of 7 families. *American Journal of Medical Genetics, 7,* 471–479.

Paul, R., Cohen, D., Breg, W., Watson, M., & Herman, S. (1984). Fragile X syndrome: Its relations to speech and language disorders. *Journal of Speech and Hearing Disorders, 49,* 326–336.

Rogers, R., & Simensen, R. (1987). Fragile X syndrome: A common etiology of mental retardation. *American Journal of Mental Deficiency, 91,* 445–449.

Turner, G., Brookwell, R., Daniel, A., Selikowitz, M., & Zilibowitz, M. (1980). Heterozygous expression of X-linked mental retardation and X-chromosome marker fra(x) (q27). *New England Journal of Medicine, 303,* 662–664.

Turner, G., Opitz, J. M., Brown, W. T., et al. (1986). Conference report: Second international workshop on fragile X and on X-linked mental retardation. *American Journal of Medical Genetics, 23,* 11–68.

Wolf-Schein, E., Sudhalter, V., Cohen, I., et al. (1987). Speech-language and the fragile X syndrome: Initial findings. *ASHA, 29,* 351–39.

Turner Syndrome
(XO Syndrome)

■ Characteristics
Dysmorphology

short stature

ovarian dysgenesis resulting in amenorrhea and infertility

congenital lymphedema of neck, hands, or feet

neck webbing

left sided heart defect or coarctation of the aorta

low posterior hairline

widely spaced nipples/broad chest

cubitus valgus

dysplastic nails

pigmented nevi

sensorineural hearing loss

narrow maxilla/palate

relative micrognathia

Turner syndrome was first described extensively by Turner in 1938. Cytogenic confirmation that this syndrome was due to a missing X chromosome occurred in 1959 (Ford, Jones, Polani, de Almeida, & Briggs, 1959). Characteristics are variable with age of presentation but include (see list):

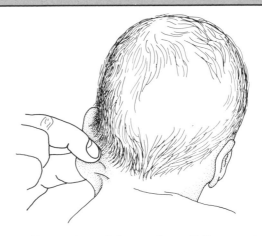

Excess skin over the neck in a newborn with Turner syndrome.

Short stature and amenorrhea may be the clinical presentation in the adolescent. This illustration also demonstrates the increased carrying angle at the elbows.

Edema of the foot may be one of the few manifestations in the newborn.

Low posterior hairline.

45

Hearing

Anatomical deformities of the auricles and hearing loss are common among individuals with Turner syndrome (Caldarelli, 1977). It has been reported that more than 80 percent of individuals with Turner syndrome have anomalous auricles. The most common deformities include low set ears, elongated ears, cup shaped ears, and thick ear lobes (Caldarelli, 1977; Heller 1965; Smith, 1976; Stratton, 1965). Anderson and colleagues (1969) reported audiometric results for 79 individuals with Turner syndrome. The authors observed a sensorineural hearing loss in 64 percent of the subjects. An additional 11 percent of the patients had a conductive hearing loss and 12 percent displayed a mixed (conductive and sensorineural) hearing loss.

The sensorineural hearing loss displayed by individuals with Turner syndrome is typically mild to moderate in severity, and bilaterally symmetrical. Typically, the audiogram is basin-shaped with a dip in hearing sensitivity occurring in the midfrequency range (between 250 and 4000 Hz). Hearing thresholds in the crest of the dip may range from 20 to 70 dB HL (the median value being 35 dB HL). In some cases, the hearing sensitivity is not better at high audiometric frequencies (Anderson et al, 1969; Szpunar & Rybak, 1968).

Severe sensorineural hearing loss is observed in fewer than 10 percent of individuals with Turner syndrome (Anderson et al., 1969). Moreover, hearing loss is rarely present at birth. The sensorineural component of the hearing loss is observed only after the individuals have reached at least 10 years of age. Little progression of hearing loss is observed during adulthood. These findings suggest that the sensorineural hearing loss associated with Turner syndrome is degenerative rather than congenital (Anderson et al., 1969).

Children with Turner syndrome seem to be predisposed to middle ear infections (Stratton, 1965; Szpunar & Rybak, 1968). Middle ear pathology is most prevalent during infancy and childhood (i.e., before age 10). Anderson and colleagues reported that 68 percent of adult patients with Turner syndrome had serious middle ear infections during childhood. In a few cases, recurrent middle ear infections were reported among older children and adults.

Speech

Oral abnormalities include relative retrognathia, high arched palate, and underdevelopment of the maxilla. Early eruption of teeth and smaller teeth with short roots have been noted as oral-dental signs. Cleft palate has also been recognized in the syndrome (Gorlin & Pindborg, 1964; Ogiuchi et al., 1985; Szpunar & Rybak, 1968).

Little information concerning speech and language is available for patients with this syndrome. The data that are available suggest that about 10 percent have some degree of mental retardation, auditory imperception, and hearing loss. Some individuals are at risk for language and learning disabilities, including written, verbal, and mathematical skills (Nielsen, Sillesen, Sorenson, & Sorenson, 1979; Sparks, 1984). Sparks (1984) has noted that girls with XO syndrome are less likely to need speech and language intervention than those with other sex-linked chromosome abnormalities. Some behavioral and psychiatric problems have been reported for male patients with sex chromosome disorders.

More extensive neuropsychological testing has been done with Turner syndrome than with some of the other sex chromosome anomalies. Evidence suggests more widespread right hemisphere dysfunction and even bilateral problems. Frontal lobe deficits would explain attentional deficits in female patients. These may also affect mathematical reasoning and organizational skills in general. In addition, results of auditory and visual evoked response testing during complex information processing commonly indicate the presence of right temporal and frontal lobe and left hemisphere problems. Thus, speech and language problems of both nonverbal and verbal areas, including auditory-verbal short term memory, receptive language skills, and speech production deficits may occur. This suggests that both auditory and visual problems may exist among individuals with this syndrome (Pennington & Smith, 1983).

Although most individuals with this syndrome show some form of speech and language disability, the deficits may be subtle and are subject to environmental influences. Few data are presently available to describe the average case or range of difficulties. The literature suggests that deficits in cognitive function, attentional factors, and hearing difficulties add to the overall problems.

Management

Genetics and Medical

Nondisjunction of chromosomes in a gamete leads to an XO chromosome constitution in approximately 1 in 2,500 in the female population. For reasons unclear, the majority of XO conceptuses are miscarried, but those surviving to birth show relatively mild characteristics. There is no strong association with increased maternal age and the condition is usually of sporadic occurrence in families. The empirical recurrence risk is very low, but prenatal diagnosis may be an option to some couples.

Expert endocrine management of the ovarian dysfunction should be sought to optimize adolescent development and attainment of ultimate height potential.

Turner syndrome may also result from chromosomal mosaicism or translocation, but these will not be discussed here.

Hearing

Because children with Turner syndrome are predisposed to having middle ear infections, a program to monitor middle ear function using an otoadmittance test battery should be instituted. Otologic consultation should be made available upon request. Amplification may be recommended in cases of prolonged or recurrent middle ear disease. Close audiological monitoring of hearing sensitivity is recommended during preadolescence and puberty. Conventional and appropriate hearing health care services should be provided to adults who have a sensorineural hearing loss. Enhancement of physical appearance by plastic surgery for canthal folds, protruding auricles, and especially for webbed neck should be given serious consideration prior to school age (Smith, 1976).

Speech

Early diagnosis of the cognitive, linguistic, auditory, and visual abilities of individuals with the syndrome appears warranted. Special attention to the behavioral deficits and consistent environmental stimulation programs appear necessary in those children who are at risk. Medical and dental care will be necessary to ameliorate oral-facial problems detected at birth or in early childhood. Special attention should be given to ongoing hearing testing in order that verbal information may be processed appropriately. Visual deficits may also be treated early to prevent delays in development of nonverbal skills.

Prognosis

With management of possible cardiac problems and ovarian dysfunction, the medical prognosis is very good. Infertility may lead to psychological problems, thus highlighting the need for early positive supportive counseling. Intelligence is usually within the normal range.

The sensorineural hearing loss associated with Turner syndrome appears to develop during the childhood and preadolescent years. However, there are indications that the hearing loss remains stable after puberty (Anderson et al., 1969).

In general, individuals with this syndrome will demand management of cognitive and language deficits. Early attention to these problems and continued evaluation improvements should result in a fair prognosis for those individuals whose deficits are not severe.

■ References

Anderson, H., Filipsson, R., Fluur, E., Koch, B., Lindsten, J., & Wedenberg, E. (1969). Hearing impairment in Turner's syndrome. *Acta Oto-Laryngologica* (Suppl. 247), 5–26.

Caldarelli, D. D. (1977). Congenital middle ear anomalies associated with craniofacial and skeletal syndromes. In B. F. Jaffe (Ed.), *Hearing loss in children: A comprehensive text.* Baltimore: University Park Press.

Ford, C. E., Jones, K. W., Polani, P. E., Almeida, J. D. de, & Briggs, J. H. (1959). A sex chromosome anomaly in a case of gonadal dysgenesis (Turner's Syndrome). *Lancet, 1,* 711–713.

Gorlin, R., & Pindborg, J. (1964). *Syndromes of the head and neck.* New York: McGraw-Hill.

Heller, R. H. (1965). The Turner phenotype in the male. *Journal of Pediatrics, 66,* 48–63.

Nielsen, J., Sillesen, I., Sorensen, A. M., & Sorensen, K. (1979). Follow-up until ages 4 to 8 of 25 unselected children with sex chromosome abnormalities compared with sibs and controls. *Birth Defects, 15,* 15–73.

Ogiuchi, H., Takano, K., Tanaka, M., et al. (1985). Oro-maxillofacial development in patients with Turner's syndrome. *Endocrinology Japan, 32,* 881–890.

Pennington, B. F., & Smith, S. S. (1983). Genetic influences on learning disabilities and speech and language disorders. *Child Development, 54,* 369–387.

Smith, D. W. (1976). *Recognizable patterns of human malformation: Genetic embryologic and clinical aspects.* Philadelphia: W. B. Saunders.

Sparks, S. (1984). *Birth defects and speech and language disorders.* San Diego: College-Hill Press.

Stratton, H. J. M. (1965). Clinical records: Gonadal dysgenesis and the ears. *Journal of Laryngology and Otology, 79,* 343–346.

Szpunar, J., & Rybak, M. (1968). Middle ear disease in Turner's syndrome. *Archives of Otolaryngology, 87,* 52–58.

Turner, H. J. (1938). A syndrome of infantilism, congenital webbed neck, and cubitus valgus. *Endocrinology, 23,* 566.

Chapter 3

Single Gene Syndromes

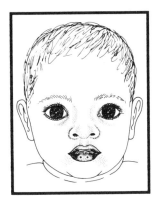

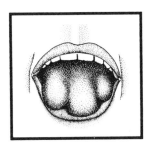

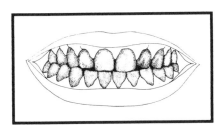

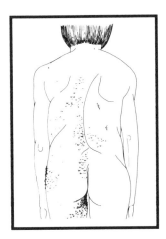

Autosomal Dominant Diseases

Alport Syndrome ■

Apert Syndrome ■

Branchio-Oto-Renal Syndrome ■

Crouzon Syndrome ■

Ectrodactyly-Ectodermal ■
Dysplasia-Clefting Syndrome

Neurofibromatosis ■

Noonan Syndrome ■

Osteogenesis Imperfecta ■

Stickler Syndrome ■

Treacher Collins Syndrome ■

Van Der Woude Syndrome ■

Waardenburg Syndrome ■

Autosomal Recessive Diseases

Jervell and Lange-Nielsen Syndrome ■

Laurence-Moon-Biedl Syndrome ■

Mucopolysaccharidoses Syndromes ■

Oro-Facial-Digital Syndrome Type II ■

Pendred Syndrome ■

Refsum Syndrome ■

Riley-Day Syndrome ■

Usher Syndrome ■

X-Linked Diseases

Oto-Palatal-Digital Syndrome ■

Wildervanck Syndrome ■

Alport Syndrome
(Hereditary Nephritis and Deafness)

■ Characteristics
Dysmorphology

chronic nephritis

sensorineural hearing loss

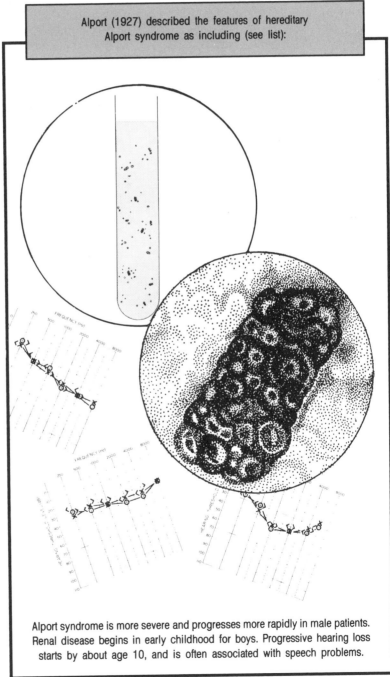

Alport (1927) described the features of hereditary
Alport syndrome as including (see list):

Alport syndrome is more severe and progresses more rapidly in male patients.
Renal disease begins in early childhood for boys. Progressive hearing loss
starts by about age 10, and is often associated with speech problems.

The renal disease is characterized by progressive ultrastructural changes of the glomerular capillary basement membranes with an absence of the immune phenomena seen in other glomerular diseases (Hasstedt, Atkin, & San Juan, 1986). Expression of the disease process in relation to renal problems and sensorineural hearing loss tends to be more severe in male than in female patients. Male patients are usually diagnosed (74 percent) as having the disease before age 6. Diagnosis at this young age is usually done by urinalysis, with those affected showing hematuria and signs of nephropathy (see Figures 3–1 and 3–2). Prior to the introduction of hemodialysis and kidney transplants, most male patients died by age 30, whereas female patients suffered only hypertension, edema during pregnancy, and a slow progressive hearing loss through a normal life span (Gubler et al., 1981; Feingold et al., 1985).

Hearing

Bilateral progressive sensorineural hearing impairment is one of the major features associated with Alport syndrome (Alport, 1927) and accounts for approximately one percent of genetically based hearing impairment in the general population (Konigsmark & Gor-

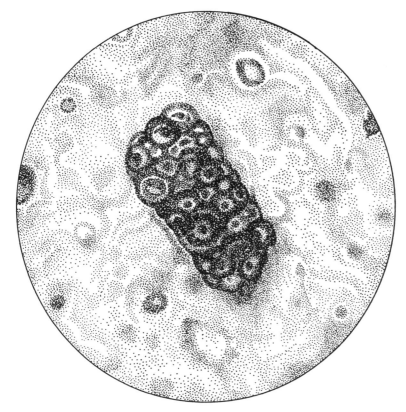

FIGURE 3–1:
Routine urinalysis is often the first indicator of renal pathology.

FIGURE 3–2:
Microscopic examination of urine may reveal red blood cell or granular casts.

lin, 1976). The hearing impairment associated with Alport syndrome occurs with greater frequency in male patients and begins with gradual onset at about age 10. In a study of seven families affected with Alport syndrome, Cassidy, Brown, Cohen, and DeMaria (1965) identified hearing impairment in 55 percent of male family members and 40 percent of female family members under investigation.

The temporal bone pathology associated with Alport syndrome has been relatively well documented (Johnsson & Arenberg, 1981; Schuknecht, 1980). In general, these histologic studies have failed to demonstrate a consistent pattern of pathologic change (Schuknecht, 1980). Included among the various changes described are loss of cochlear neurons and hair cells, atrophy of the stria vascularis and spiral ligaments, and endolymphatic hydrops. Johnsson and Arenberg (1981) have provided a detailed account of histopathologic and audiometric studies on four cases of Alport syndrome. Despite similar audiometric profiles for two of the cases, rather different histopathologic changes were observed.

The audiological manifestations of Alport syndrome have been described in detail by Rintlemann (1976), Miller, Joseph, Cozad, and McCabe (1970), and more recently by Gleeson (1984). In his review paper, Rintlemann (1976) identified three audiometric configurations in Alport syndrome patients, including what he labeled as "trough-shaped" (47.1 percent), "sloping" (41.2 percent) and "flat" (11.7 percent) (see Figure 3–3a, b, c). From the majority of cases reviewed, it was concluded that both degree and configuration of hearing loss was bilaterally symmetrical. Among the 51 audiograms reviewed, hearing loss ranged from mild to severe, with pure tone averages across all subjects of 33 dB for those with flat audiograms, 42 dB for those with the trough-shaped configuration, and 50 dB for the sloping hearing losses. Finally, Rintlemann documented the progression in hearing sensitivity for three brothers with Alport syndrome over a period of 4 years, 10 months. The three brothers were aged, 7, 8, and 10 at the time of the initial studies. For all three boys, the pure tone average hearing levels became poorer in both ears within the 4 years, 10 month interval. Individual ear pure tone average hearing level changes of between 8 and 34 dB were observed. With the exception of one ear for one of the brothers, word recognition ability remained relatively stable at a constant sensation level at high performance levels (86 to 98 percent correct).

Speech

Typical speech problems affecting these hearing impaired individuals would be lack of articulation precision with high frequency consonants such as fricatives, difficulty monitoring vocal frequency and intensity levels, and control of stress effort of speech production. Because the syndrome progresses quickly in male patients, they are more at risk for hearing related speech problems than are female patients.

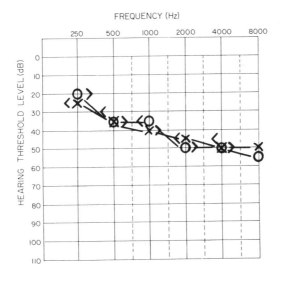

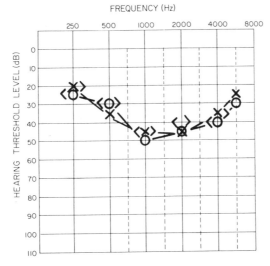

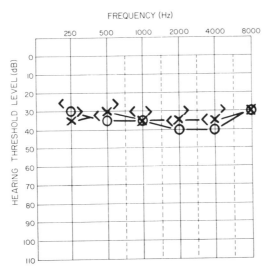

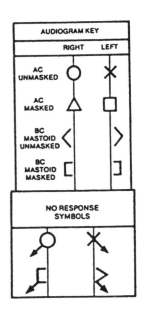

FIGURE 3–3a, b, c: *Characteristic pure-tone audiometric findings associated with Alport syndrome.*

Management

Genetics and Medical

It was noted in Alport's original description of this syndrome that it occurred in both sexes and in successive generations. The majority of families with Alport syndrome demonstrated autosomal dominant inheritance. Therefore, an affected person has a 50 percent chance for passing the gene on to his or her children. Genetic heterogeneity exists as some families demonstrate x-linked inheritance. A careful review of the family pedigree is essential in differentiating between modes of inheritance.

Medical concerns center around maintenance of normal renal function. Hemodialysis or kidney transplantation may be necessary in severe cases of nephritis.

Hearing

Rintlemann (1976) strongly recommended that a comprehensive audiological evaluation become part of the routine investigation of patients with renal disorders, as the findings can contribute important data toward identifying the presence of Alport syndrome. In view of the progressive nature of this disorder, careful and frequent monitoring of the audiological status and amplification program is strongly advised.

Speech

Traditional aural rehabilitation programs, hearing aid fitting, and speech therapy may be necessary for persons with the most rapidly progressing form of the disease (Gleeson, 1984).

Prognosis

The prognosis is poor to guarded for male patients, and fair to good for affected female patients. Because subgroups apparently exist within the syndrome, careful long-term follow-up is necessary. Male patients will profit from early intervention for aural rehabilitation and speech therapy, whereas female patients may not need intervention from communication specialists until later in life.

■ References

Alport, A. C. (1927). Hereditary familial congenital hemorrhagic nephritis. *British Medical Journal, 1,* 504–506.

Cassidy, G., Brown, K., Cohen, M., & DeMaria, W. (1965). Hereditary renal dysfunction and deafness. *Pediatrics, 35,* 967–979.

Feingold, J., Bois, E., Chompret, A., Broyer, M., Gubler, M-C., & Grunfeld, J-P. (1985). Genetic heterogeneity of Alport syndrome. *Kidney International, 27,* 672–677.

Gleeson, M. J. (1984). Alport's syndrome: Audiological manifestations and implications. *The Journal of Laryngology and Otology, 98,* 449–465.

Gubler, M., Levy, M., Broyer, M., Naizot, C., Gonzalez, G., Perrin, D., & Habib, R. (1981). Alport's syndrome. *The American Journal of Medicine, 70,* 493–505.

Hasstedt, S. J., Atkin, C. L., & San Juan, A. C. (1986). Genetic heterogeneity among kindreds with Alport syndrome. *American Journal of Human Genetics, 38,* 940–953.

Johnsson, L. G., & Arenberg, I. (1981). Cochlear abnormalities in Alport's syndrome. *Archives of Otolaryngology, 107,* 340–349.

Konigsmark, B. W., & Gorlin, R. J. (1976). *Genetic and metabolic deafness.* Toronto: W. B. Saunders.

Miller, G. W., Joseph, D. J., Cozad, R. L., & McCabe, B. F. (1970). Alport's syndrome. *Archives of Otolaryngology, 92,* 419–432.

Rintlemann, W. F. (1976). Auditory manifestations of Alport's disease syndrome. *Transactions of the American Academy of Ophthalmology and Otolaryngology, 82,* 375–387.

Schuknecht, H. F. (1980). Dysmorphogenesis of the inner ear. *Birth Defects, 16,* 47–71.

Apert Syndrome
(Acrocephalosyndactyly Type I)

■ Characteristics
Dysmorphology

craniosynostosis

synostosis and/or syndactyly
of the hands and feet

midfacial hypoplasia

strabismus

prominent eyes

frontal bossing

hearing loss

speech difficulties

Apert syndrome is a distinctive acrocephalosyndactyly syndrome initially reported by Wheaton (1894) and more recently reviewed by Blank (1960). It is characterized by (see list):

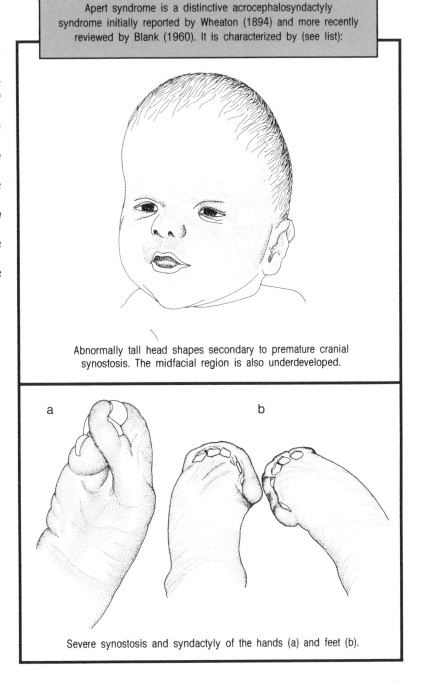

Abnormally tall head shapes secondary to premature cranial synostosis. The midfacial region is also underdeveloped.

a   b

Severe synostosis and syndactyly of the hands (a) and feet (b).

The syndactyly or synostosis commonly involves complete fusion of the second, third, and fourth digits. The craniosynostosis usually affects the coronal suture, which results in the short anterior-posterior diameter of the skull, high forehead, and flattened frontal and occipital bones. The associated midfacial hypoplasia contributes to the shallow orbits, proptosis, hypertelorism, and small nose. Occasionally an infant may also show large fontanels.

Normally, during the first two years of life, intracranial volume and brain weight greatly increase. Due to increased intracranial pressure of the growing brain, compensatory growth leads to changes in the size, shape, and posture of the cranial structures (Gorlin & Pindborg, 1976).

Hearing

Although few studies have investigated the hearing abilities of individuals with Apert syndrome, there are some indications that many individuals with this syndrome display a hearing loss of sufficient magnitude to interfere with verbal communication (Elfenbein, Waziri, & Morris, 1981). Conductive hearing loss are predominant among this population (Konigsmark & Gorlin, 1976). Elfenbein and colleagues (1981) reported a history of otitis media among four subjects with Apert syndrome. The severity of the conductive component varied considerably among their subjects and the level of hearing sensitivity ranged from hearing within normal limits (i.e., SRT of 15 dB HL) to a moderately severe hearing loss (i.e., SRT of 55 dB HL). Fixation of the middle ear ossicles (i.e., the stapes) as well as other middle ear anomalies resulting in a conductive hearing loss have also been observed among this population (Bergstrom, Neblett, & Hemenway, 1972; Lindsay, Black, & Donnelly, 1975; Peterson & Pruzansky, 1974; Solomon, Medencia, Pruzansky, & Kreiborg, 1973).

In summary, the hearing abilities of individuals with Apert syndrome should be similar to the audiologic profile of individuals with Crouzon syndrome or cleft palate (consult those sections in this book for more information concerning typical audiological manifestations).

Speech

In the oral cavity, the hard palate is highly arched with a noticeable median groove. Associated with the maxillary hypoplasia is compression of the dental arch with a V-shaped defect, a "Byzantine-shaped" hard palate, irregular positioning of the teeth, marked thickening of the alveolar process, and class III malocclusion. There are also lateral swellings containing acid mucopolysaccharide deposits. The soft palate may also appear abnormally long or thickened relative to the dimensions of the oral cavity. Such malformations are found in about one-half the cases, with approximately 25 to 30 percent having a cleft of the soft palate or bifid uvula (Peterson & Pruzansky, 1974).

The oral configuration, particularly the long, thick palate and the small nasopharynx, leads toward hyponasality, mouth breathing, and forward posturing of the tongue. Because of the abnormalities of the oral cavity and the malalignment of the jaws, individuals with this syndrome are likely to have difficulty producing alveolar consonants, such as /s/, /z/, and /t/ and /d/. In addition, a severe Angle's class III malocclusion may cause difficulty with labial dental sounds (e.g., /f/, /v/). Compensatory action by the tongue may be necessary, but may cause both acoustic and cosmetic errors of sound production. Minimal data are available regarding language development, but case studies have suggested that language function is most directly related to the cognitive level, hearing status, and age of initial operation to correct the craniofacial problems (Elfenbein et al., 1981; Sparks, 1984). Voice quality problems may relate to the oral pharyngeal configurations and the resultant upward pull on the supralaryngeal structures (Peterson–Falzone, 1981; Witzel, 1983).

Management

Genetics and Medical

This syndrome occurs approximately once in 160.000 live births (Gorlin & Pindborg, 1976). Most cases occur sporadically and are likely due to spontaneous autosomal dominant mutations. Few instances of parent to child transmission are reported, due to lowered reproductive fitness. The recurrence risk for offspring of an affected individual is 50 percent. Midtrimester prenatal diagnosis of the digital or skull malformation may be possible in centers experienced in detailed ultrasound diagnostic imaging.

Neonatal management should be aggressive. Mental retardation is not considered an intrinsic part of this syndrome. Later management should be coordinated by a multidisciplinary craniofacial team. Surgical correction of digital fusion will allow for optimal hand function.

Hearing

Conventional otological and audiological management should be used to treat the various types of conductive hearing loss associated with Apert syndrome. When otological treatment is not possible, an amplification system (including a bone conduction hearing aid) should be considered.

Speech

The most common operative procedure is the LeFort III osteotomy, used to correct the midface deficiencies of persons with Apert syndrome. In a number of cases, correction of the articulation errors and hyponasal resonance balance occur following the operation (McCarthy, Coccaro, & Schwartz, 1979; Witzel, 1983). The correction of the malocclusion and the normalization of the oropharynx allows for more efficient tongue mobility and increased movement of the soft palate for differentiation of nasal and nonnasal sounds. In older patients, speech therapy must follow surgical alteration of the oral-facial area in order to modify poor habits developed from years of overcompensation.

Prognosis

Prognosis is dependent upon the severity of the disorder, the cognitive capacities of the patient, and the associated problems affecting hearing and speech production. In a majority of cases, surgical intervention at an earlier age will allow for cranial and facial growth that will foster normal habits of speech development. Careful monitoring of the hearing status will also allow the person to receive articulation and resonance information without distortion. Such factors will promote communication competency.

■ References

Bergstrom, L. M., Neblett, L. M., & Hemenway, W. G. (1972). Otologic manifestations of acrocephalosyndactyly. *Archives of Otolaryngology, 96,* 117–123.

Blank, C. E. (1960). Apert's syndrome (a type of acrocephalosyndactyly). Observations on a British series of thrity-nine cases. *Annals of Human Genetics, 24,* 151–164.

Elfenbein, J., Waziri, M., & Morris, H. L. (1981). Verbal communication skills in six children with craniofacial anomalies. *Cleft Palate Journal, 18,* 59–64.

Gorlin, R., & Pindborg, J. (1976). *Syndromes of the head and neck.* New York: McGraw-Hill.

Konigsmark, B. W., & Gorlin, R. J. (1976). *Genetic and metabolic deafness.* Toronto: W. B. Saunders.

Lindsay, J. R., Black, F. O., & Donnelly, W. N. (1975). Acrocephalosyndactyly (Apert syndrome). Temporal bone findings. *Annals of Otology, 84,* 174–178.

McCarthy, J. G., Coccaro, P. J., & Schwartz, M. D. (1979). Velopharyngeal function following maxillary advancement. *Plastic and Reconstructive Surgery, 64,* 180–189.

Peterson, S., & Pruzansky, S. (1974). Palatal anomalies in the syndromes of Apert and Crouzon. *Cleft Palate Journal, 11,* 394–402.

Peterson–Falzone, S. (1981). Impact of communicative disorders on otolaryngologic care of patients with craniofacial anomalies. *Otolaryngologic Clinics of North America, 14,* 895–915.

Solomon, L. M., Medencia, M., Pruzansky, S., & Kreiborg, S. (1973). *Teratology, 8,* 287–292.

Sparks, S. (1984). *Birth defects and speech and language disorders,* (pp. 53–56). San Diego: College Hill Press.

Wheaton, S. W. (1894). Two specimens of congenital cranial deformity in infants associated with fusion of the fingers and toes. *Transcriptions of the Pathological Society of London, 45,* 238.

Witzel, M. A. (1983, April). Speech problems in craniofacial anomalies. *Communicative Disorders, 8,* 45–59.

Branchio-Oto-Renal Syndrome
(BOR Syndrome)

■ Characteristics
Dysmorphology

The association of hearing loss, renal dysplasia, and ear anomalies found in branchio-oto-renal syndrome was first described by Melnick, Bixler, Silk, Yune, and Nance (1975). The incidence of BOR syndrome is approximately 1 in 40,000 individuals (Fraser, Sproule, & Halal, 1980). Fraser, Ling, Clogg, and Nogrady (1978) further set forth the clinical and genetic characteristics, which include (see list):

hearing loss

preauricular pits

branchial fistulas or cysts

anomalous pinna

renal dysplasia (hypoplasia of kidneys and/or anomalies of the collecting system)

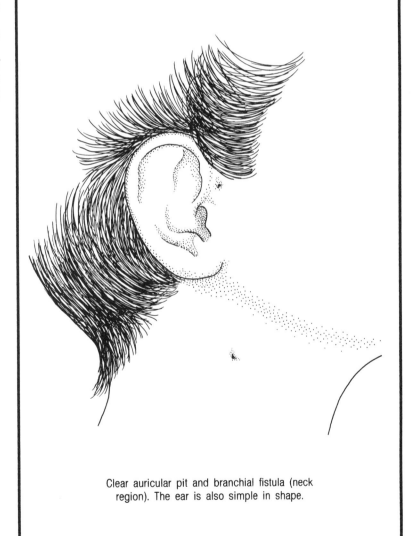

Clear auricular pit and branchial fistula (neck region). The ear is also simple in shape.

Hearing

Various anomalies of the outer, middle, or inner ear exceed 40 percent (Smith, 1982). Malformations of the auricles range from cupped, flattened, or hypoplastic pinnae to severe microtia. The external auditory canal may be narrow, malformed, or slanted upward (Fraser et al., 1978; Melnick et al., 1975). In the middle ear, the ossicles may be displaced or malformed (Bourguet, Mazeas, & LeHuérou, 1966; Karmody, 1974). The stapes may be fused or unconnected (McLaurin, Kloepfer, Laguaite, & Stallcup, 1966; Rowley, 1969). Finally, the apex of the cochlea may be hypoplastic (e.g., Mondini deformity; Melnick et al., 1975), or the stria vascularis may show atrophy or dysplasia (Smith, Dyches, & Loomis, 1984).

Offspring of individuals who have BOR syndrome are very likely (80 percent) to have a hearing impairment. The type and degree may vary considerably (Fraser et al., 1978). The onset of the hearing loss can occur from early childhood to young adulthood (Fraser et al., 1978). The hearing loss associated with BOR syndrome is not progressive, but in some cases, the hearing may deteroiate during adulthood (Gimsing & Dyrmose, 1986; Smith et al., 1984).

The type of hearing loss exhibited by individuals with BOR syndrome can be conductive (30 percent), sensorineural (20 percent), or mixed (50 percent). The degree of hearing loss may range from mild to severe (Gimsing, 1987).

Speech

The primary communication handicap associated with BOR syndrome is hearing loss. The condition may therefore be expected to have an adverse effect on the development and maintenance of age appropriate speech and language skills, especially if it is progressive and of early onset.

Management

Genetics and Medical

This is an autosomal dominant syndrome with widely variable expressivity and penetrance (Gimsing, 1987; Rollnick, & Kaye, 1985; Smith et al., 1984). When this condition is suspected, renal ultrasonography can be sensitive in the detection of renal malformations. An intravenous pyelogram will usually be required to rule out dysplasia of the collecting system. Because a small percentage of patients will go on to renal failure, monitoring of renal function is an important aspect of ongoing management. Renal dysplasia may also be detected prenatally, but diagnosis should only be attempted by experienced personnel, as variability of the syndrome may lead to false negative conclusions.

Hearing

All individuals with preauricular pits and branchial clefts should be seen by an otologist and nephrologist (Fraser et al., 1980; Smith et al., 1984).

Smith and colleagues (1984) recommended that young children with BOR syndrome who have middle ear malformations should have surgical reconstruction postponed until the temporal bone assumes a mature size and function. Amplification should be instituted during the preoperative interval.

Family members of individuals with BOR syndrome should be evaluated for evidence of BOR dysplasia. Periodic evaluation may be required to detect the evolution of age-related signs and symptoms (Smith et al., 1984).

Speech

Management of speech and language difficulties associated with hearing losses in BOR syndrome will necessarily vary according to type of loss, severity of loss, and age of onset. Aural rehabilitation attempts focus on development of skills when onset is in early childhood, and on maintenance of speech and articulation skills when hearing loss onset occurs after normal development of speech and language skills.

Prognosis

Prognosis necessarily varies with degree and type of expressivity. A more favorable prognosis is associated with later onset of hearing loss and absence of significant renal disease. Early identification and follow-up of hearing impairment, and appropriate involvement of speech and language and special education personnel are necessary to optimize the development of communicative skills.

■ References

Bourguet, J., Mazeas, R., & LeHuéron, Y. (1966). De l'atteinte des deux premières fentes et des deux premières arcs branchiaux. *Revue d'Otoneurologie et ophthalmologie, 38,* 162–175.

Fraser, F. C., Ling, D., Clogg, D., & Nogrady, B. (1978). Genetic aspects of the BOR syndrome-branchial fistulas, ear pits, hearing loss, and renal anomalies. *American Journal of Medical Genetics, 2,* 241–252.

Fraser, F. C., Sproule, J. R., & Halal, F. (1980). Frequency of the branchio-oto-renal (BOR) syndrome in children with profound hearing loss. *American Journal of Medical Genetics, 7,* 341–349.

Gimsing, S. (1987). The BOR syndrome as a possible neurocristopathy. *Ear, Nose and Throat Journal, 66,* 154–158.

Gimsing, S., & Dyrmose, J. (1986). Branchio-oto-renal dysplasia in three families. *Annals of Otology, Rhinology and Laryngology, 95,* 421–426.

Karmody, C. S. (1974). Autosomal dominant first and second branchial arch syndrome. A new inherited syndrome? In D. Bergsma (Ed.), *Malformation syndromes* (pp. 31–40). Miami: Symposia Specialists for The National Foundation–March of Dimes.

McLaurin, J. W., Kloepfer, H. W., Laguaite, J. K., & Stallcup, T. A. (1966). Hereditary branchial anomalies and associated hearing impairment. *Laryngoscope, 76,* 1277–1288.

Melnick, M., Bixler, D., Silk, K., Yune, H., & Nance, W. E. (1975). Autosomal dominant branchiootorenal dysplasia. *Birth Defects Original Article Series, 11, 5,* 121–128.

Rollnick, B., & Kaye, C. (1985). Hemifacial microsomia and the branchio-oto-renal syndrome. *Journal of Craniofacial Genetics and Developmental Biology, Supplement 1,* 287–295.

Rowley, P. T. (1969). Familial hearing loss associated with branchial fistulas. *Pediatrics, 44,* 978–985.

Smith, D. W. (1982). *Recognizable patterns of human malformations* (3rd ed.). Philadelphia: W. B. Saunders.

Smith, P. G., Dyches, T. J., & Loomis, R. A. (1984). Clinical aspects of the branchio-oto-renal syndrome. *Otolaryngology — Head and Neck Surgery, 92,* 468–475.

Crouzon Syndrome
(Craniofacial Dysostosis)

■ Characteristics
Dysmorphology

craniosynostosis

midfacial/maxillary hypoplasia

shallow orbits with exopthalmos

ocular hypertelorism

strabismus

"parrot-like" nose

frontal bossing

brachycephaly

hearing loss

communication difficulties

First reported by Crouzon (1912), Crouzon syndrome is most easily recognized by premature craniosynostosis, particularly of the coronal suture. However, recent research (Burdi, Kusnetz, Venes, & Gebarski, 1986) has implicated the sphenoethmoidal synchondroses of the midline cranial base as the primary site of pathogenesis. This results in characteristic craniofacial development (Gorlin & Pindborg, 1976), which includes (see list):

The variation in expression can be great in the newborn. Ptosis may be one of the few features with very little difference in overall head shape. Later on, the shape of the skull may resemble that seen in Apert syndrome.

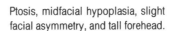

Ptosis, midfacial hypoplasia, slight facial asymmetry, and tall forehead.

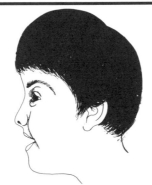

Irregular head shape with short diameter from front to back.

Hearing

It is estimated that approximately one-third to one-half of individuals with Crouzon syndrome have a hearing loss (Boedts, 1967; Clerc & Deumier, 1958; Selder, 1973). Although there is very little documented evidence, several causes of hearing loss have been hypothesized. They include: (1) stenosis, atresia, and other deformities of the external auditory canal; (2) deformities of the middle ear cavity (including anomalies of the ossicular chain, ankylosis of the stapes, or other ossicular fixation) as well as Eustachian tube dysfunction; and (3) hyperostosis of the inner table of the skull, causing a narrowing of the internal meatus, which in turn results in a functional impairment due to the compression of the nerves and blood vessels to the labyrinth (Baldwin, 1968).

The type of hearing loss most often associated with Crouzon syndrome is conductive. The nature of the conductive hearing impairment may vary widely and may be considered in two distinct categories: acquired conductive hearing loss and congenital conduction problems (Caldarelli, 1977). Acquired ear diseases may be similar to those typically observed among individuals with cleft palate (i.e., recurrent chronic otitis media and its concomitant Eustachian tube dysfunction) or anomalies in the growth patterns of the skull which may cause distortions and/or obstruction of the nasopharynx as well as obstructions of the Eustachian tube. Congenital conduction problems might include: stenosis or atresia of the external auditory canal, absence of the tympanic membrane or an unusually positioned tympanic membrane, hypoplastic tympanic cavity and ossicular chain fixation (Caldarelli, 1977). The degree of conductive hearing loss reported among individuals with Crouzon syndrome may range from mild to moderately severe. For example, chronic otitis media may result in a mild to moderate hearing loss whereas atresia of the outer ear canal would produce a moderately severe conductive hearing loss.

Some cases of sensorineural hearing loss associated with Crouzon syndrome have been reported. However, the information available from individuals with Crouzon syndrome is limited and it is usually impossible to relate the cause of the sensorineural hearing loss directly to Crouzon syndrome (Selder, 1973).

Speech

Maldevelopment of the maxilla is most severe in the premaxillary region, causing a crowding of the maxillary teeth. The result of the small maxillary area in relation to the normal mandibular arch may cause the lower teeth to occlude over the upper teeth in a prognathic or Angle's class III relationship. In addition, the palate is described as being high arched or "Byzantine"-shaped, and may be filled with hyperplastic soft tissue and marked with a median furrow. The shallow oropharynx may also cause obligatory mouth breathing and a forward carriage of the tongue often seen in these individuals. Frequently, the presence of an abnormally long and thick soft palate may contribute to blockage of the nasopharynx and cause resonatory and nasal respiration problems (Gorlin & Pindborg, 1976; Kellin, Chaudhry, & Gorlin, 1960; Peterson–Falzon & Pruzansky, 1974).

The major components of the communication difficulties lie in the degree of palatal involvement, the severity of the oral cavity misalignment, the cognitive function, and the type and degree of hearing loss. In instances where the synostosis is apparent and untreated until later in life, cognitive or linguistic deficits may occur and be represented by problems in receptive and recognition vocabulary and reduced levels of syntax acquisition (Elfenbein, Waziri, & Morris, 1981). More often, oral distortions of sibilants, fricatives, and affricative sound elements are present in conversational speech (Elfenbein et al., 1981; Peterson–Falzone, 1982; Witzel, 1983). In addition, the shallow oropharynx and relatively long thick palate and maxillary hypoplasia may result in hyponasal (denasal) speech quality (Peterson–Falzone, 1982). In patients with clefts of the hard or soft palate, hypernasality and nasal air emission of high oral pressure speech sounds (i.e., /p/, /s/) will result. Hearing impairment that accompanies the disease will also delay development of speech and language.

There are no published data obtained from a large group of patients concerning the range of severity in communication. Certainly, the speech, language, and quality disturbances noted in the literature support a wide range of differences in communication abilities (Witzel, 1983).

Management

Genetics and Medical

Crouzon syndrome is autosomal dominant with extremely variable expression. Careful examination of family members is indicated, as not all individuals with craniofacial dysostosis will have problems requiring medical or surgical attention. Parents of a proband have almost a zero recurrence risk if the child truly represents a spontaneous mutation. However, the recurrence risk may be as high as 50 percent if either parent is documented to have subtle features of this syndrome or there exists a positive family history. Success with prenatal diagnosis has been variable, as craniosynostosis or other features may not be apparent in pregnancy. The neonatal clinical picture may even include very large fontanelles and widely split cranial sutures. In those cases, premature suture fusion may occur after birth.

Complete examination is indicated as there is overlap between the Crouzon and Saethre-Chotzen syndrome (also autosomal dominant). The latter is associated with some degree of brachydactyly, syndactyly, and broadness of the thumbs and large toes. Coronal craniosynostosis may also be part of other acrocephalosyndactyly syndromes (e.g., Apert syndrome) with different genetic implications or even of nongenetic etiology (secondary to in utero head constraint).

Hearing

When applicable, it may be possible to surgically reconstruct the outer or middle ear. In other cases, traditional otological approaches used to treat problems of conductive hearing loss may be required to treat problems of chronic otitis media. Finally, when otological management is not possible, amplification may be recommended. In some cases, a bone conduction hearing aid may be required rather than a conventional air conduction amplification device.

Speech

Early recognition of the disorder and prompt medical and behavioral intervention are essential to allow normal development and to minimize possible psychosocial trauma to the individual and the family. Cephalometric roentgenograms, axial and paraxial reformatted CT scans, and newly developed 3-D surface imaging of CT scans are useful tools for anatomical investigations of the structures beneath the skin of the skull, brain, globes, and muscles of facial region (Marsh & Vannier, 1987). These imaging techniques assist in the diagnosis, treatment planning, and longitudinal evaluation of medical and dental management.

Early craniofacial surgery (Munro, 1975) with young infants or children may aid in normalization of cognitive function and the orofacial structures related to speech production. Assessment in the cognitive, linguistic, speech-resonance, and hearing areas should continue through the early school age years. Surgical procedures to close a cleft of the hard or soft palate may be necessary in infancy to aid in the development of normal articulation and language production.

In addition, Le Fort osteotomy procedures are often used with older patients with Crouzon syndrome to correct midface deficiencies. These patients often have articulation errors related to occlusal defects or oral anomalies along the alveolar and palatal ridge or have resonance imbalance of the hyponasal type related to the unusually long or thick velum and the hypoplastic pharynx (Witzel, 1983). These orofacial surgical techniques may be expected to improve not only the appearance of these patients, but articulation and resonance balance as well. Traditional speech therapy following surgical management may aid in retraining the timing and placement of the articulators in cases where adaptation does not take place spontaneously.

Deficits in speech production and language development detected at an early age must be important management considerations. Although a delay in direct articulation therapy may occur relative to dental and surgical management designed to make major alterations in the orofacial environment, general language stimulation should take place as soon as possible. Observed hearing deficits should be dealt with in order that this problem does not further complicate communication development (Elfenbein et al., 1981).

Prognosis

The age of onset and the severity of the craniosynostosis influences the type and degree of complications, including craniofacial disfigurement, hearing loss (Selder, 1973), speech and language difficulties (Elfenbein et al, 1981; Peterson–Falzone, 1982; Witzel, 1983), visual impairment (Gorlin & Pindborg, 1976), and intellectual deficits (Noetzel, Marsh, Palkes, & Gado, 1985; Powazek & Billmeier, 1979). The types of hearing loss typically associated with Crouzon syndrome are not progressive (Northern & Downs, 1984).

Prognosis will depend upon the severity of the symptoms and the age at which surgical, dental, and communication management takes place. Early surgical correction of the deficits will promote brain growth, normal facial development, and improved oral-velopharyngeal action. Continued assessment of the behavioral aspects of cognitive and linguistic function will aid in selecting the appropriate placement in various therapies. With more normal appearance from early years, many psychosocial problems will be limited and progress will be determined by individual patient motivation (Peterson–Falzone, 1982).

■ References

Baldwin, J. L. (1968). Dysostosis craniofacialis of Crouzon. *Laryngoscope, 78,* 1660–1676.

Boedts, D. (1967). La surdite dans la dysostose craniofaciale ou maladie de Crouzon. *Acta Oto-Rhino-Laryngologica Belgica, 21,* 143–155.

Burdi, A. R., Kusnetz, A. B., Vernes, J. L., Gebarski, S. S. (1986). The natural history and pathogenesis of the cranial coronal ring articulations: Implications in understanding the pathogenesis of the Crouzon craniostenotic defects. *Cleft Palate Journal, 23,* 28–39.

Caldarelli, D. D. (1977). Congenital middle ear anomalies associated with craniofacial and skeletal syndromes. In B. F. Jaffe (Ed.), *Hearing loss in children: A comprehensive text* (pp. 310–340). Baltimore, MD: Williams & Wilkins.

Clerc P., & Deumier, R. (1958). La surdite dans les dysplasies osseuses et les dysmorphies cranio-faciale. *Annales d'Oto-Laryngologie et De Chirurgie Cervico-Faciale, 75,* 852–874.

Crouzon, O. (1912). Dysostose cranio-faciale hereditaire. Bulletins et memoires. *Societe Medicale Des Hopitaux de Paris, 33,* 545.

Elfenbein, J. L., Waziri, M., & Morris, H. L. (1981). Verbal communication skills of six children with craniofacial anomalies. *Cleft Palate Journal 18,* 59–64.

Gorlin, R. & Pindborg, J. (1976). *Syndromes of the head and neck.* New York: McGraw-Hill.

Kellin, E. E., Chaudhry, A. P., & Gorlin, R. J. (1960). Oral manifestations of Crouzon's disease. *Oral Surgery, Oral Medicine and Oral Pathology, 13,* 1245–1248.

Marsh, J. L., & Vannier, M. W. (1987). The anatomy of the cranio-orbital deformities of craniostenosis: Insights from 3-D images of CT scans. *Clinical Plastic Surgery, 14,* 49–60.

Munro, I. R. (1975). Orbito-cranio-facial surgery: The team approach. *Plastic Reconstructive Surgery, 55,* 170–176.

Noetzel, M. J., Marsh, J. L., Palkes, H., & Gado, M. (1985). Hydrocephalus and mental retardation in craniosynostosis. *Journal of Pediatrics, 107,* 885–892.

Northern, J. L., & Downs, M. P. (1984). *Hearing in children* (3rd ed.). Baltimore, MD: Williams & Wilkins.

Peterson–Falzone, S. (1982). Resonance disorders in structural defects. In N. J. Lass, L. V. McReynolds, J. L. Northern, & D. E. Yoder (Eds.), *Speech, language and hearing, Vol. II: Pathologies of speech and language* (pp. 526–555). Philadelphia: W. B. Saunders.

Peterson–Falzone, S., & Pruzansky, S. (1974). Palatal anomalies in the syndromes of Apert and Crouzon. *Cleft Palate Journal, 11,* 394–402.

Powazek, M., & Billmeier, G. J. (1979). Assessment of intellectual development after surgery for craniofacial dysostosis. *American Journal of Diseases of Children, 133,* 151–153.

Selder, A. (1973). Hearing disorders in children with otocraniofacial syndromes. ASHA Report 8. *Orofacial anomalies: Clinical and research implications* (pp. 95–110). Rockville, MD: American Speech & Hearing Association.

Witzel, M. A. (1983). Speech problems in craniofacial anomalies. *Communicative Disorders, VIII, 4,* 45–59.

Ectrodactyly-Ectodermal Dysplasia-Clefting Syndrome
(EEC Syndrome)

■ Characteristics
Dysmorphology

ectrodactyly or split hand (milder cases having syndactyly only)

ectodermal dysplasia (light, sparse hair, lacrimal duct defects, hypoplastic nails, partial anodontia, hyperkeratosis, absent sebaceous glands)

cleft lip or cleft palate

occasional hearing loss and/or anatomical anomalies of the external ear

Ectrodactyly-ectodermal dysplasia-clefting syndrome was initially described by Rudiger, Haase, and Passarge in 1970. It has become characterized as a complex developmental abnormality which affects both ectodermal and mesodermal elements of development (Leibowitz & Jenkins, 1984; Pashayan, Pruzansky, & Soloman, 1974). Kuster, Majewski, and Meinecke (1985) emphasized the variability of this syndrome, with features including (see list):

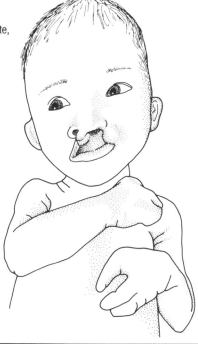

Features of EEC syndrome: sparse hair, cleft lip and palate, and ectrodectyly.

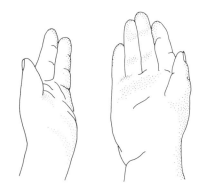

Hand defects may be unilateral in EEC syndrome.

Hearing

Although not a cardinal characteristic of the syndrome, cases of hearing loss among individuals with EEC syndrome have been reported (Konigsmark & Gorlin, 1976). Further, many case reports of individuals with EEC have noted anomalies associated with the external ear. The most common anatomical abnormality of the ear consists of small, malformed auricles (Freire–Maia, Cat, & Rapone-Gaidzinski, 1977; Kaiser–Kupfer, 1973; Robinson, Wildervanck, & Chiang, 1973).

A low-frequency mild-moderate conductive hearing loss is often observed among individuals with EEC syndrome (Konigsmark & Gorlin, 1976; Swallow, Gray, & Harper, 1973). The conductive hearing loss is usually secondary to chronic middle ear infections commonly observed among individuals with a cleft palate. In some cases, perforated tympanic membranes have been reported (Robinson et al., 1973). Also, there is a report of one individual with EEC syndrome, an absent stapes, and a partly absent incus (Robinson et al., 1973).

The incidence of sensorineural hearing loss among individuals with EEC syndrome is not well documented (Konigsmark & Gorlin, 1976). Freire–Maia and colleagues (1977) reported a profound sensorineural hearing loss in a case study of a female child age 7 years 6 months. The same report cited studies in which the incidence of sensorineural hearing loss accompanying ectodermal dysplasias with limb malformations was 60 percent. Wildervanck (1963) reported two cases with ectrodactyly (brothers) who displayed a sensorineural hearing impairment ranging from a mild loss at low frequencies to a profound loss at frequencies above approximately 2000 Hz. It was hypothesized that sensorineural hearing impairments associated with ectodermal dysplasias reflect elements of the inner ear that have an ectodermal origin (Freire–Maia et al., 1977).

Speech

Although Kuster, Majewski, and Meinecke (1985) stated that no symptom of EEC syndrome is obligatory, both complete and incomplete forms of the syndrome appear to be characterized by clefting of the lip or palate that may be unilateral or bilateral (Bixler, Spivack, Bennett, & Christian, 1971; Gellis & Feingold, 1976; Goodman & Gorlin, 1977; Gorlin, Pindborg, & Cohen, 1976; Pashayan, Pruzansky, & Soloman, 1974; Sedano, Sauk, & Gorlin, 1977; Soloman, Cook, & Klipfel, 1987). Of 19 cases involving clefting reported by Bixler and colleagues (1971), 11 had bilateral cleft lip and palate, 4 had left unilateral cleft lip and palate, 1 had unilateral right cleft lip and palate, and 3 had cleft of the lip only. Similarly, Sedano, Sauk, and Gorlin (1977) reported that clefting of the lip is generally bilateral, and that bilateral cleft lip and palate occurs in about 50 percent of affected individuals. Although Gorlin and colleagues (1976) agreed, they did report that clefting is absent in some cases.

The existence of cleft lip, if repaired, should not present any difficulties with respect to speech production. Typical cleft related problems will be associated with clefting of the palate. These include problems in childhood with sucking, swallowing, nasal regurgitation, nasal air emission, hypernasality, and the potential for compensatory articulations. The frequent occurrence of a conductive hearing loss may be expected to hamper the development of language. Although infrequent, mental retardation may be associated with developmental delay, poor gross motor control, learning disability, and school performance problems.

Management

Genetics and Medical

The majority of family pedigree data support an autosomal dominant gene with variable expression and incomplete penetrance (Sedano et al., 1977). Care must be taken to distinguish this condition from others such as the Rapp–Hodgkin form of ectodermal dysplasia (which also includes cleft palate). Due to the variability in expression, careful study of family members may be required to help differentiate between an inherited form and a spontaneous mutation in an apparently isolated case. It is difficult to exclude genetic heterogeneity with some cases suggested to be autosomal recessive (Gellis & Feingold, 1976).

Individuals who have the gene for EEC syndrome are at a 50 percent risk of passing it on to any child. Prenatal diagnosis of severe ectrodactyly is possible by careful midtrimester ultrasonography.

As in other syndromes that involve ectodermal dysplasia, a relative lack of sweat glands predisposes an individual to heat stroke. In severe cases, brain damage is a possible consequence, so individuals must be promptly treated with antipyretics during febrile episodes and avoid extremely warm/hot environmental situations.

Hearing

Hearing aids accompanied with a comprehensive aural rehabilitation progam will be required for individuals with a sensorineural hearing loss associated with EEC syndrome. Otological and audiological management and treatment of conductive hearing loss typically associated with cleft palate will be required for individuals with the syndrome.

Speech

Surgical treatment of clefts of the lip or palate may be performed to normalize the oral, nasal, and pharyngeal area for aid in developing speech and swallowing activities. Speech and language therapy will be a part of the team treatment process with these patients (O'Dwyer, Renner, & Fergusen, 1984). Articulation and language development may be expected to be compromised by the presence of hearing loss or intellectual handicaps. In the latter case, the input of special education professionals should be sought.

Prognosis

Any severe hand malformation will require close follow-up and possible orthopedic management. There are no published data on the incidence or range of severity of intellectual handicaps. However, it is interesting to speculate whether any developmental problem might be due to heat sensitivity and periods of hyperthermia secondary to the lack of sweat glands.

Timely and successful orofacial surgery will improve the chances for normal speech and language development. Early intervention and close follow-up by speech and language pathologists and special educators can be expected to optimize speech and language performance.

■ References

Bixler, D., Spivack, J., Bennett, J., & Christian, J. (1971). The ectrodactyly-ectodermal dysplasia-clefting (EEC) syndrome. *Clinical Genetics, 3,* 43–51.

Freire–Maia, N., Cat, I., & Rapone–Gaidzinski, R. (1977). An ectodermal dysplasia syndrome of alopecia, onychodysplasia, hypohidrosis, hyperkeratosis, deafness and other manifestations. *Human Heredity, 27,* 127–133.

Gellis, S., & Feingold, M. (1976). The EEC syndrome. *American Journal of Diseases of Children, 130,* 653–654.

Goodman, R., & Gorlin, R. (1977). *Atlas of the face in genetic disorders.* St. Louis: C. V. Mosby.

Gorlin, R., Pindborg, J., & Cohen, M. (1976). *Syndromes of the head and neck.* New York: McGraw-Hill.

Kaiser–Kupfer, M. (1973). Ectrodactyly, ectodermal dysplasia and clefting syndrome. *American Journal of Ophthalmology, 76,* 992–998.

Konigsmark, B. W., & Gorlin, R. J. (1976). *Genetic and metabolic deafness.* Philadelphia: W. B. Saunders.

Kuster, W., Majewski, F., & Meinecke, P. (1985). EEC syndrome without ectrodactyly. *Clinical Genetics, 28,* 130–135.

Leibowitz, M., & Jenkins, T. (1984). A newly recognized feature of ectrodactyly, ectodermal dysplasia, clefting (EEC) syndrome: Comedone naevus. *Dermatology, 169,* 80–85.

O'Dwyer, M., Renner, R., & Fergusen, F. (1984). Overdenture treatment — One aspect of the team approach for the EEC syndrome patient. *Journal in Pedodontology, 8,* 192–205.

Pashayan, H. M., Pruzansky, S., & Solomon, L. (1974). The EEC syndrome. *Birth Defects, 10*(7), 105–127.

Robinson, G. C., Wildervanck, L. S., & Chiang, T. P. (1973). Ectrodactyly, ectodermal dysplasia and cleft lip-palate. Its association with conductive hearing loss. *Journal of Pediatrics, 82,* 107–109.

Rudiger, R., Haase, W., & Passarge, E. (1970). Association of ectrodactyly ectodermal dysplasia and cleft lip palate. *American Journal of Diseases of Children, 120,* 160–163.

Sedano, H., Sauk, J., & Gorlin, R. (1977). *Oral manifestations of inherited disorders.* Boston: Butterworths.

Solomon, L., Cook, B., & Klipfel, W. (1987). The ectodermal dysplasias. *Dermatological Clinics, 5,* 231–237.

Swallow, J. N., Gray, O. P., & Harper, P. S. (1973). Ectrodactyly, ectodermal dysplasia and cleft lip and palate (EEC syndrome). *British Journal of Dermatology,* (Suppl. 9), 54–56.

Wildervanck, L. S. (1963). Perceptive deafness associated with split-hand and foot — A new syndrome? *Acta Genetica, 13,* 161–169.

Neurofibromatosis
(Von Recklinghausen Disease; NFM)

■ Characteristics
Dysmorphology

*café-au-lait spots:
more than five spots
greater than 1.5 cm
in diameter*

axillary freckling

*dysplastic tumors —
cutaneous or subcutaneous;
biopsy confirmation of
a neurofibroma*

Neurofibromatosis is an autosomal dominant disorder that has a wide range of expressivity and occurs in 1 out of every 2,500 to 3,300 births (Goodman & Gorlin, 1977, p. 164). Von Recklinghausen (1882) described this syndrome as being "characterized by abnormal cutaneous pigmentation and numerous tumors developing in association with elements of both the central and peripheral nervous system." The cardinal features include (see list):

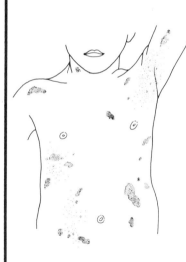

Cutaneous manifestations include café-au-lait spots and axillary freckling.

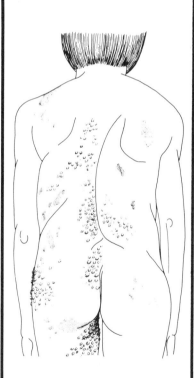

On occasion, neurofibromas may be present. Scoliosis is also a relatively common musculoskeletal finding.

Neurofibromatosis is usually a slowly progressive disease with physical manifestations often present at birth. In one series (Fienman & Yakovac, 1970), 43 percent of 46 patients manifested signs at birth; 63 percent by age one. The most common presenting signs are café-au-lait spots or neurofibromas, which usually occur disparately rather than simultaneously. Pigmentary changes occur in 95 percent of patients. Café-au-lait spots are macular, usually smooth bordered, and found most often on the trunk and unexposed areas. Axillary freckling is uncommon in the general population. Areas of hypopigmentation similar to those in tuberous sclerosis may also be observed. An estimated one percent have a bathing suit or giant hairy nevus.

Neurofibromas are tremendously variable in number and size, and usually grow with age. If present before age 10, the prognosis is usually poorer. They may increase in size and number in times of stress, infection, or with puberty or pregnancy. Plexiform neurofibromas are associated with overgrowth phenomena and compression effects. Seizures, macrocephaly, and hydrocephalus are relatively rare central nervous system complications. Tumors can involve any nerve, but the risk of sarcomatous degeneration is low (approximately five percent).

Neurofibromatosis is considered to be a primary disorder of neural crest derivation. Electron microscopic studies have shown that tumors arise from cellular elements of a peripheral nerve (Schwann cells, fibroblasts, perineural cells).

Although pheochromocytoma and secondary hypertension are present in one to five percent of cases, precocious puberty is the most common endocrine manifestation during childhood. Central nervous system neurofibromatosis with acoustic neuroma involvement is probably a distinct entity. Skeletal manifestations include scoliosis as the most common developmental anomaly.

Hearing

Central neurofibromatosis was recently established as an entity marked by a bilateral acoustic neuroma and one or more café-au-lait spots or subcutaneous neurofibromas (Eldridge, 1981).

Hearing impairment may accompany both the peripheral and the central form of neurofibromatosis (Deutsch, 1984; Eldridge, 1981; Kanter, Eldridge, Fabricant, Allen, & Koerberg, 1980). The most prevalent form of hearing loss associated with neurofibromatosis is bilateral acoustic neuroma (Holt, 1978).

Neurofibromatosis is a dynamic pathological process with physical manifestation often present at birth and becoming more prevalent with age (Fienman & Yakovac, 1970). Acoustic neuromas are rarely reported in children (Fienman & Yakovac, 1970). Typically, acoustic neuromas (i.e., bilateral tumors) associated with this syndrome are first reported during the second decade of life. This differs from cases of unilateral acoustic neuromas, not associated with neurofibromatosis, which occur most frequently during the fourth decade (Hitselberger & Hughes, 1968).

The only consistent feature of neurofibromatosis is the progression of the disease and the increase in the number or size of hyperpigmented skin lesions and tumors in all sites, especially the skin. The tremendous diversity of neurofibromatos makes it impossible to describe a singular natural history of the disorder (Riccardi, 1981a, b). The number and progression of noncutaneous tumors in neurofibromatosis appear unrelated to the number, size, and distribution of the cutaneous and subcutaneous neurofibromas (Riccardi, 1981a, b). However, it has been reported that the disease may worsen at the time of puberty and during pregnancy (Holt, 1978).

Bilateral acoustic neuromas are the hallmark of central neurofibromatosis. They also occur in two to four percent of cases with peripheral neurofibromatosis (Kanter et al., 1980). Other otologic manifestations of neurofibromatosis include: facial nerve neurofibroma and meningioma; stapes fixation by tumors of the perilymphatic space; middle ear neurofibroma of Jacobson's nerve or Arnold's nerve; plexiform neurofibroma of the external ear (Holt, 1978). In addition, vestibular dysfunction due to ataxia (Hughes, Sismanis, Glasscock, Hayes, & Jackson, 1982) and tinnitus (Deutsch, 1984) have also been reported.

Generally, audiological or otological manifestations of individuals with acoustic tumors associated with neurofibromatosis are similar to persons with unilateral tumors not related to the syndrome (Hitselberger & Hughes, 1968). The patient with bilateral acoustic tumors typically complains of slowly progressive hearing loss in one or both ears. Tinnitus may accompany the hearing loss (Holt, 1978). Because the vestibular function is often reduced bilaterally, the patient may complain of ataxia (especially in the dark) rather than true vertigo (Hughes et al., 1982).

Audiometric testing usually reveals bilateral sensorineural hearing loss (often asymmetric) and the results suggest retrocochlear pathology (i.e., poor speech recognition scores in quiet or in noise, positive tone decay, low SISI scores, type III or IV Bekesy tracings) (Holt, 1978). There is no correlation between the size of the acoustic neuroma and the degree of hearing loss (Holt, 1978). Thus, pure-tone sensitivity may be normal despite a relatively large tumor. Brainstem evoked response audiometry usually shows prolonged central conduction time or abnormal waveform morphology (Hughes et al., 1982). The presence of one tumor is a strong indicator of the presence of a second, contralateral tumor (Holt, 1978).

Smaller neurofibromas may develop in the perilymphatic space. These may lead to a conductive hearing loss as the stapes of the footplate becomes fixated. Tumors have also been reported to grow into the external auditory canal to demonstrate a second cause of conductive loss (Holt, 1978).

Speech

The head, neck, and oral region is affected in approximately 2 to 10 percent of the cases (Koblin & Reil, 1975; Epstein, Schubert, & Hatcher, 1983). Head and neck manifestations occur almost exclusively unilaterally, and may include hypoplasia of the maxilla, mandible, and temporomandibular joint (Koblin & Reil, 1975). Oral neurofibromas appear typically as discrete nodules involving the tongue buccal mucosa, and (rarely) the alveolar ridge. However, Epstein and colleagues (1983) stated that oral lesions are usually asymptomatic. Freelander, Swerdloff, and Mongiardo (1956) referred to tongue involvement as being the more common oral manifestation. These lesions may be diffuse (i.e., macroglossia) or localized. The most common intracranial finding is the development of central nervous system tumors (White, Smith, Bigler, Brooke, & Schauer, 1986).

Of the cases evaluated by White and colleagues, EEG data were normal in 18 percent, seizures were noted in 12 percent, and mental retardation was noted in seven percent. Riccardi (1981a) reported intellectual handicap in 40 percent of a sample population, with frank mental retardation in two to five percent.

Two categories of manifestation of this syndrome are reported to affect speech and language. The first relates to central nervous system disorders, whereas the second concerns peripheral mechanical factors affecting voice, speech, and resonance. Speech characteristics that may be related to central nervous system involvement are breathiness, roughness, monopitch, vocal tremor, monoloudness, as well as hypernasality, imprecise consonant production, and a reduced rate of speaking (Riccardi, 1981a). Krueger, Weisberger, and Bailantyne (1979) also noted that paresis of the last four cranial nerves may lead to dysphagia, hoarseness, shoulder drop, and tongue atrophy. Further, intellectual handicaps reported by Riccardi (1981b) have been associated with developmental delay, learning disability, hyperactivity, poor gross motor control, and school performance problems.

Mechanically oriented speech disabilities may involve neurofibromas in laryngeal, pharyngeal, and oral regions (White et al., 1986). It is important to note that it may be difficult to differentiate conclusively between the mechanical and neurological components.

The fact that expressivity and penetrance of this syndrome is variable leads to a wide range of intellectual, language learning, and speech problems. Further, there appear to be two age peaks of severe clinical problems (White, et al., 1986). The early period (age 1 to 10) involves more central nervous system involvement and mental retardation, whereas the later age period (age 36 to 50) involves more tumor growth and malignancy.

Management

Genetics and Medical

Neurofibromatosis is a confirmed autosomal dominant trait. Perhaps 50 percent of cases are due to spontaneous mutation, but careful examination of family members is needed to help exclude mild expression. Almost all carriers of this gene are expected to manifest some sign or symptom. Recent advances in recombinant DNA technology have allowed mapping of this gene to chromosome 17 (Barker et al., 1987). It is hoped that further molecular and protein studies will elucidate the exact nature of the gene and its function in the pathogenesis of neurofibromatosis.

Formal audiological and eye (including visual field) assessments are recommended yearly. Routine examinations should pay particular attention to scoliosis and blood pressure.

Hearing

The otological and audiological management of individuals with neurofibromatosis include audiological monitoring, surgical intervention, and aural rehabilitation.

Systematic audiological monitoring is recommended for individuals who are known to be afflicted with the syndrome but do not display any clinical signs of acoustic neuromas (Hughes et al., 1982). Individuals with clinically confirmed acoustic tumors should undergo surgery as soon as possible unless the resection of the acoustic neuroma is contraindicated for other medical reasons (Holt, 1978; Hughes et al., 1982; Kanter et al., 1980). Genetic counseling should be provided to the afflicted individual as well as to members of his or her family (Deutsch, 1984; Kanter et al., 1980). In cases of bilateral tumors, it is recommended that the individual be provided with speech and reading training and/or manual communication lessons (Hughes et al., 1982; Kanter et al., 1980).

Speech

Development of both speech and language should be monitored and managed in children with neurofibromatosis. Treatment regimens will be largely behavioral in nature, although surgical intervention may be required in some cases. Specifically, large tumors of the tongue, although not common, would be expected to interfere with tongue movement during articulation, and surgical excision may be necessary. In such cases, therapy directed toward compensatory articulatory patterns would benefit the patient.

The speech and language pathologist is more likely to be called on to deal with speech and language problems arising from central nervous system involvement. Managment of speech disorders such as imprecise consonants and reduced rate may follow well-documented techniques that are applicable to dysarthric patients (Johns, 1978). Management of learning disability or poor school performance may involve special education personnel. If learning disabilities are minimal, patients may be mainstreamed. Conversely, more severe involvement may entail enrollment in a self-contained specific learning disability class. Children with neurofibromatosis and central nervous system involvement may require continuing special education through the academic years, and perhaps vocational assistance thereafter.

Prognosis

It has been estimated that 60 to 75 percent of all patients with neurofibromatosis need related medical care. Neurofibromatosis can be compatible with a full and useful life. Early diagnosis, awareness of potential complications, and early treatment of complications are crucial for lowering morbidity and mortality.

One should be optimistic that early and correct treatment can help avoid or minimize potential problems. Although sometimes referred to as the "Elephant Man Disease," that individual probably had a distinct diagnosis known as the Proteus syndrome.

The likelihood of preserving any hearing after the removal of acoustic tumors is considerably greater if the tumor is small (i.e., not larger than 1.0 cm in size). Hearing preservation with total tumor removal is doubtful if the lesion is larger than 2.0 cm (Holt, 1978; Hughes et al., 1982; Kanter et al., 1980). The morbidity and mortality associated with removal of medium and larger tumors in individuals with neurofibromatosis has a higher risk (33 percent) than isolated acoustic tumors (seven percent). This may be attributed to the multiple central nervous system anomalies associated with neurofibromatosis (Holt, 1978).

Prognosis will necessarily be somewhat dependent on the severity of the disorder and type of involvement. Brasfield and Das Gupta (1972) reported that many patients with central nervous system tumors die in childhood. However, it may take more than 20 years for spinal cord involvement to develop from more peripheral neurofibromas. With respect to intellectual handicaps, Riccardi (1981b) reported that it is almost always apparent prior to enrollment in school, and that it does not worsen with time. Therefore, early intervention and close follow-up may be expected to optimize development in these individuals.

■ References

Barker, D., Wright, E., Nguyen, K., et al. (1987). Gene for Von Recklinghausen Neurofibromatosis is in the pericentromeric region of chromosome 17. *Science, 236,* 1100–1102.

Brasfield, R., & Das Gupta, T. (1972). Von Recklinghausen's disease: A clinicopathologic study. *Annals of Surgery, 175,* 86–104.

Deutsch, E. C. (1984). Von Reckinghausen's neurofibromatosis with multiple intracranial tumors. *Ear, Nose and Throat Journal, 63,* 141–148.

Eldridge, R. (1981). Central neurofibromatosis with bilateral acoustic neuroma. In V. M. Riccardi & J. J. Mulvihill (Eds.), *Advances in neurology, 29, neurofibromatosis (von Reckinghausen's disease)* (pp. 57–65). New York: Raven Press.

Epstein, J., Schubert, M., & Hatcher, D. (1983). Multiple neurofibromatosis. *Oral Surgery, 56,* 560–562.

Fienman, N. L., & Yakovac, W. C. (1970). Neurofibromatosis in childhood. *Journal of Pediatrics, 76,* 339–346.

Freedlander, A., Swerdloff, M., & Mongiardo, J. (1956). Von Recklinghausen's disease. *Oral Surgery, 9,* 9–12.

Goodman, R., & Gorlin, R. (1977). *Atlas of the face in genetic disorders.* St. Louis: C. V. Mosby.

Hitselberger, W. E., & Hughes, R. L. (1968). Bilateral acoustic tumors and neurofibromatosis. *Archives of Otolaryngology, 88,* 700–711.

Holt, R. G. (1978). ENT manifestations of von Recklinghausen's disease. *Laryngoscope, 88,* 1617–1632.

Hughes, G. B., Sismanis, A., Glasscock, M. E., III, Hayes, J. W., & Jackson, C. G. (1982). Management of bilateral acoustic tumors. *Laryngoscope, 92,* 1351–1359.

Johns, D. (1978). *Clinical management of neurogenic communicative disorders.* Boston: Little, Brown & Co.

Kanter, W. R., Eldridge, R., Fabricant, R., Allen, J. C., & Koerberg, T. (1980). Central neurofibromatosis with bilateral acoustic neuroma: Genetic, clinical and biochemical distinction from peripheral neurofibromatosis. *Neurology, 30,* 851–859.

Koblin, I., & Reil, B. (1975). Changes in the facial skeleton in cases of neurofibromatosis. *Journal of Maxillofacial Surgery, 3,* 23–27.

Krueger, W., Weisberger, E., & Bailantyne, A. (1979). Plexiform neurofibroma of the head and neck. *American Journal of Surgery, 138,* 517–520.

Riccardi, V. M. (1981a). Neurofibromatosis: An overview and new directions in clinical investigations. In V. M. Riccardi & J. J. Mulvihill (Eds.), *Advances in neurology, 29, neurofibromatosis (von Recklinghausen's disease)* (pp. 1–10). New York: Raven Press.

Riccardi, V. M. (1981b). Von Recklinghausen neurofibromatosis. *The New England Journal of Medicine, 305,* 1617–1627.

Von Recklinghausen, F. (1882). Ueber die multiplen fibroma der haut und ihre Beziehung zu den multiplen Neuromen. Berlin: A. Hirschwald.

White, A., Smith, R., Bigler, C., Brooke, W., & Schauer, P. (1986). Head and neck manifestations of neurofibromatosis. *Larynogoscope, 96,* 732–737.

Noonan Syndrome
(Turner-Like Syndrome)

■ Characteristics
Dysmorphology

*congenital heart disease
(typically pulmonic stenosis)*

short stature

*facial anomalies
(hypertelorism, ptosis of
eyelids, epicanthal folds,
low set anomalous ears,
neck webbing)*

*skeletal abnormalities
(cubitus valgus,
hemivertebrae)*

cryptorchidism

*mental retardation
(50 to 60 percent
of patients)*

Noonan syndrome has a clinical phenotype similar to that seen in Turner syndrome. Important distinguishing features are that Noonan syndrome occurs in both sexes and that it is not associated with a sex chromosome imbalance. Noonan syndrome is heterogeneous, but there exists a growing consensus toward at least one distinct clinical entity within this phenotypic spectrum (Allanson, Hall, Hughes, Preus, & Witt, 1985).

The initial clinical description of this syndrome, as distinct from Turner syndrome, was by Noonan and Ehmke (1963). Children with Noonan syndrome are characterized by (see list):

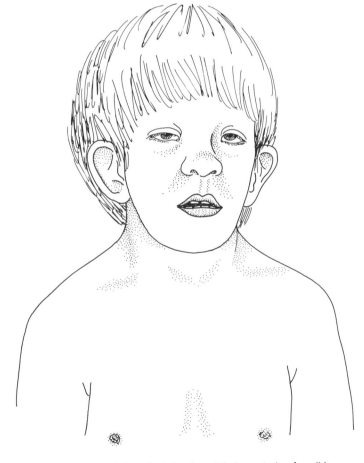

Facial dysmorphology includes hypertelorism, ptosis of eyelids, epicanthal folds, low set ears, and mild webbing of the neck.

Hearing

Abnormally shaped ears is one of the most prominent features associated with Noonan syndrome. Nora, Nora, Sinha, Spangler, and Lubs (1974) reported ear anomalies in 78 percent of their subjects with Noonan syndrome. Prominent pinnae, low set auricles, and posteriorly rotated ears are among the most common ear anomalies reported (Baird & DeJong, 1972; Collins & Turner, 1973; Hopkins–Acos & Bunker, 1979; Nora et al., 1974). Anomalies of the ears observed in Noonan syndrome are usually more pronounced than the anomalies observed in individuals with Turner syndrome (Nora et al., 1974).

Hearing loss associated with Noonan syndrome is not common. Some reports indicate the possibility of a sensorineural hearing loss. However, little detail is provided regarding the degree of hearing loss or the audiometric configuration of the afflicted individuals (Nora et al., 1974; Smith, 1976). A mild low frequency conductive hearing loss was reported in one case of a preschool aged child with Noonan syndrome (Hopkins–Acos & Bunker, 1979).

Speech

Information concerning speech and language deficits for individuals with this syndrome are limited. However, considering the percentage of individuals with orofacial defects and the prevalence of developmental delays, cognitive differences, and hearing loss, associated speech and language problems are not unexpected. One study (Nora et al., 1974) noted that approximately 72 percent of the 25 children studied had articulation problems and that 12 percent had hearing difficulties. Hopkins–Acos and Bunker (1979) undertook a case study of a male child with Noonan syndrome. They reported reduced motor development, limited sensorimotor experiences, general language delay, and mild hearing impairment. They also noted nasalization of normally oralized sounds in his phonetic repertoire. Another case study of a child with Noonan syndrome was reported by Sparks (1984). Not unlike the child described by Hopkins–Acos and Bunker (1979), Sparks noted that her patient was delayed in developing gross and fine motor skills and receptive language. He had a short attention span and a severe delay in expressive language development. His speech production skills were limited. He used two to three word utterances and had difficulty with initial consonant sound production. Hypernasality occured, although there was no overt cleft of the hard or soft palate. There was, however, insufficient movement of the lateral pharyngeal wall structures. Although IQ scores were not available in either case study, other researchers have noted substantial problems with cognitive function in this syndrome (Money & Kalus, 1979).

The intelligence quotients for one group of subjects with Noonan syndrome (Money & Kalus, 1979) showed a range of IQ from a low of 64 to a high of 127, with the median group score falling in the "low average to high average" range. The authors noted that special attention should be given to subtest scores on cognitive testing to determine whether discrepancies occur between verbal and performance scores and to note the types of difficulties within each subtest area. Subjects in this study were bimodally rather than continuously distributed according to stature and there was a tendency for verbal praxic disparity and lower full scale IQs to be associated with the short stature group.

Although the data concerning speech, language, and cognitive function are few, the suggestion is that there is a wide range of abilities among this group (Sparks, 1984). Mild forms of the syndrome may have gone unnoticed as part of the nonaffected population, whereas severe cases only may have been referred for further medical and behavioral evaluation. Certainly, those with several obvious signs of the disorder may have speech and language problems that place them in the moderately to severely delayed range.

Management

Genetics and Medical

The incidence of Noonan syndrome has been estimated to be between 1 in 1,000 to 1 in 2,500 live births (Nora & Fraser, 1981). Mendez and Opitz (1985) have suggested a frequency of 1 in 1,000 of severely affected individuals and perhaps 1 in 100 with a mild expression of the syndrome. The high incidence and great variability of the syndrome have led researchers to speculate about heterogeneity. Almost one-half of the individuals are free from heart defects and both sexes tend to be generally fertile. Although sporadic cases have been noted, approximately three-fourths of the cases have shown direct parent-child transmission. Multifactorial casual hypotheses do not satisfactorily explain the variability of expression. Some researchers lean toward autosomal dominant determination as being a better explanation than others (Allanson et al., 1985; Mendez & Opitz, 1985).

Whereas dominant transmission is evident from family history, affected individuals have a 50 percent chance to pass the gene on to their children. Although gonadal differentiation may vary, fertility is thought to be normal. The intrafamilial variability may be wide.

Many conditions need to be excluded before arriving at a diagnosis of Noonan syndrome. Cases of chromosomal mosaicism must be ruled out. There is also similarity to the William syndrome, fetal alcohol syndrome, and fetal hydantoin (Dilantin) syndrome.

Hearing

The management of any conductive or sensorineural hearing loss among individuals with Noonan syndrome should not differ from conventional treatments and rehabilitation programs provided to other individuals who are hearing impaired. Otologic and audiologic consultations, treatment, and follow-up are recommended.

Speech

Early diagnosis of individuals with Noonan syndrome and its possible effects on speech, language, and hearing is important. Given the range of problems noted in the literature, individually based therapy programs for language stimulation may be required. Care should be taken to distinguish phonological errors based upon learning from those with physical bases. Special attention should be focused on the cognitive strengths of each individual. A team approach to management of the special language learning problems is advocated.

Prognosis

Given the variability of this syndrome, prognosis will depend upon the extent of cardiovascular and central nervous system involvement. In the absence of a serious heart problem, life expectancy should be normal (Nora et al., 1974).

Individuals with mild forms of Noonan syndrome may be expected to respond well to traditional educational methods, whereas those with more numerous signs and severe forms may need special methods and individualized instruction. Early identification and management of speech and hearing problems should result in fair to moderate improvement in specific areas of deficit.

■ References

Allanson, J. E., Hall, J. G., Hughes, H. E., Preus, M., & Witt, R. D. (1985). Noonan syndrome: The changing phenotype. *American Journal of Medical Genetics, 21,* 507–514.

Baird, P. A., & DeJong, B. P. (1972). Noonan's syndrome (XX and XY Turner phenotype) in three generations of a family. *Journal of Pediatrics, 80,* 110–114.

Collins, E., & Turner, G. (1973). The Noonan syndrome: A review of the clinical and genetic features of 27 cases. *Journal of Pediatrics, 83,* 941–950.

Hopkins–Acos, P., & Bunker, K. (1979). A child with Noonan syndrome. *Journal of Speech and Hearing Disorders, 44,* 494–503.

Mendez, H. M. M., & Opitz, J. M. (1985). Noonan syndrome: A review. *American Journal of Medical Genetics, 21,* 493–506.

Money, J., & Kalus, M. E. (1979). Noonan syndrome. *American Journal of Diseases of Childhood, 133,* 846–850.

Noonan, J. A., & Ehmke, D. A. (1963). Associated noncardiac malformations in children with congenital heart disease. *Journal of Pediatrics, 63,* 468–470.

Nora, J. J., & Fraser, F. C. (1981). *Medical genetics: Principles and practices* (2nd ed.). Philadelphia: Lea & Febiger.

Nora, J. J., Nora, A. H., Sinha, A. K., Spangler, R. D., & Lubs, H. A. (1974). The Ullrich–Noonan syndrome (Turner phenotype). *American Journal of Diseases of Children, 127,* 48–55.

Smith, D. W. (1976). *Recognizable patterns of human malformation: Genetic embryologic and clinical aspects.* Philadelphia: W. B. Saunders.

Sparks, S. (1984). *Birth defects and speech and language disorders.* San Diego: College-Hill Press.

Osteogenesis Imperfecta
(Type I, Type II, Tarda)

■ Characteristics
Dysmorphology

fragile and brittle bones

blue sclera

hearing loss

dentinogenesis imperfecta

hyperelasticity of joints and ligaments

The heterogeneous group of connective tissue disorders involving bone fragility have been classified by phenotype and genetics (Sillence, Senn, & Danks, 1979). Numerous investigators have also begun to establish the molecular pathology involving collagen in bone matrix formation (Byers, Barsh, & Holbrook, 1982; Prockop, 1984; Sillence et al., 1979).

The most severe manifestation of osteogenesis imperfecta is the perinatal lethal form (type II). As its name implies, this form is usually lethal soon after birth. The relatively less severe osteogenesis imperfecta type I involves multisystem problems (Gorlin & Pindborg, 1976), including (see list):

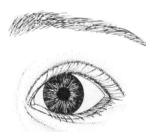

Close-up of blue sclera.

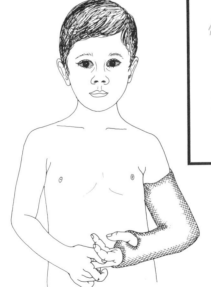

Fractures are common in childhood.

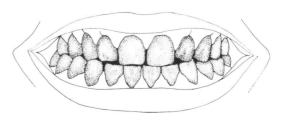

Dentinogenesis imperfecta with blue/gray coloration of the teeth.

Its incidence has been estimated at 2 to 5 per 100,000 births in different populations (McKusick, 1972). Previously, distinction was made between a tarda and a congenita form, but occurrence of both phenotypes in the same family support tremendous variability in expression of the gene responsible for type I osteogenesis imperfecta.

Hearing

All types of hearing impairment — conductive, mixed and sensorineural — have been reported to occur. Estimates of frequency of hearing loss among individuals with type I range from 26 to 60 percent (Bergstrom, 1977).

The hearing loss most frequently associated with type I results from an otosclerotic-like process that involves the stapedial footplate, as well as fibrous degeneration of the stapes and the crural fractures (Quisling, Moore, Jahrsdoerfer, & Cantrell, 1979). Many investigators have attempted to relate type I to otosclerosis. However, histopathologic and biochemical evidence fails to support a common origin and it would seem as though type I and otosclerosis are histologically distinct (Brosnan, Burns, Jahn, & Hawke, 1977; Holdsworth, Endahl, Soifer, Richardson, & Eyring, 1973; Quisling et al., 1979). Although the histopathologic patterns may be distinct, the clinical patterns of the hearing loss that accompany type I are identical to those of otosclerosis (McKusick, 1972).

The onset of the hearing loss has been reported to occur during the second or third decade of life or earlier (Riedner, Levin, & Holliday, 1980). Further, the hearing loss associated with type I may have its onset in the teens or the onset of the hearing loss may occur during pregnancy (McKusick, 1972). Conductive hearing loss is commonly associated with type I. According to Riedner, and colleagues (1980), ossicular immobility at the stapes footplate is likely a major cause of the conductive hearing deficit in type I. Sensorineural hearing loss associated with type I has also been observed. Soifer, Weaver, Endahl, and Holdsworth (1970) reported that severe sensorineural hearing loss occurred in approximately 40 percent of all cases of type I. The incidence of hearing loss increases with age of the affected person. Riedner and colleagues (1980) reported that by the seventh decade of life, all of the subjects had a hearing loss. In the same study, they observed that all of the subjects who had hearing loss and were more than 50 years of age had a hearing loss characterized by a sensorineural component (i.e., pure sensorineural or mixed hearing loss).

The hearing loss may vary from a mild subclinical conductive hearing loss to anacusis (Riedner et al., 1980). Mild to moderate conductive hearing losses (most pronounced at frequencies below approximately 1,000 Hz) have been observed among individuals in their late second or early third decade of life. High frequency sensorineural components have been reported in individuals in their fifth decade of life or older (Riedner, et al., 1980).

More than 50 percent of the individuals who have a hearing loss associated with type I display normal tympanograms. Significantly fewer will show type A_s traces associated with reduced eardrum compliance or a hypermobile type A_d tympanogram. As would be expected, acoustic reflexes are often absent among individuals with type I who have a hearing loss. Acoustic reflexes may not be observed because of mild conductive components or if there is a moderately severe hearing loss in the ear being stimulated (i.e., the stimulus ear). In some cases, diphasic acoustic reflexes (on-off effect) similar to those observed among individuals with otosclerosis have been observed among individuals with osteogenesis imperfecta tarda. It is speculated that the diphasic reflexes indicate the onset of stapes footplate fixation (Bel et al., 1976; Terkildsen, Osterhammel, & Bretlau, 1973).

Speech

As is the case in all instances where a hearing loss is present, school or job performance may be compromised. Because the hearing loss does not typically develop until the third decade of life, the hearing loss associated with osteogenesis imperfecta should not cause problems with speech and language development. However, in cases where the hearing loss is evident in young children, the risk of speech and language development problems must be considered.

Infrequently, other characteristics of this group of patients include condylar deformities, mandibular prognathism, and dislocation of the mandibular condyle. In cases where mandibular prognathism is evident, articulation development may be hampered. Abnormal mandibular and maxillary relationships could result in abnormal tongue posturing in a compensatory fashion, resulting in aberrant articulatory patterns.

Management

Genetics and Medical

Osteogenesis imperfecta type I is due to the effects of an autosomal dominant gene. Variability in expression necessitates careful history and examination, especially in apparently isolated cases. If in doubt, consultation with a medical geneticist should be sought, as molecular studies of the gene or of collagen may be indicated. Children of an affected person have a 50 percent chance of inheriting the responsible gene. Careful orthopedic follow-up can help reduce long-term morbidity related to fractures or bone deformity.

Hearing

Reconstructive surgery (i.e., stapedectomy) has been used to improve the hearing thresholds among individuals with osteogenesis imperfecta type I (Kosoy & Maddox, 1971). Alternatively, hearing aids may be used.

Speech

When hearing loss is evident in children who are developing speech and language skills, both speech and language therapy and audiologic and otologic treatment may be required. In the case of mandibular prognathism, mild cases may be addressed in speech therapy. Severe cases may benefit from surgical management plus speech therapy.

Prognosis

Children with the syndrome fall within the normal range of intelligence. Apart from the physical and physiological characteristics, educational manifestations must also be considered. As a result of bone brittleness and other factors, regular attendance at school for an osteogenesis imperfecta child may be difficult (Varni & Jaffe, 1984), although the frequency of fractures would be expected to decrease with time.

Reconstructive surgery (i.e., stapedectomy) has not been generally successful. Poor long-term results were noted in some patients who underwent stapedectomy (Brosnan et al., 1977; Kosoy & Maddox, 1971; Riedner et al., 1980). Because of the conductive component typically associated with hearing loss in type I, it is expected that individuals would benefit greatly from wearing hearing aids.

With respect to communication skills, the typical type I patient who acquires a hearing loss has already developed speech and language. Given the success of surgical and prosthetic treatment of this type of hearing loss, the prognosis for maintenance of adequate speech is good. When detected and treated early, those who develop hearing loss during the speech and language development stage should also be expected to do well. Similarly, timely attention to the severely prognathic mandible may be expected to optimize the development of appropriate articulation patterns.

■ References

Bel, J., Causse, P., Michaux, P., Cezard, R., Canut, Y., & Tapon, J. (1976). Mechanical explanation of the on-off effect (diphasic impedance change) in otospongiosis. *Audiology, 15,* 128–140.

Bergstrom, L. (1977). Osteogenesis imperfecta: Otologic and maxillofacial aspects. *Laryngoscope, 87* (Suppl. 6), 1–42.

Brosnan, M., Burns, H., Jahn, A. F., & Hawke, M. (1977). Surgery and histopathology of the stapes in osteogenesis imperfecta tarda: A report of ten cases. *Archives of Otolaryngology, 103,* 294–298.

Byers, P. H., Barsh, G. S., & Holbrook, K. A. (1982). Molecular pathology in inherited disorders of collagen metabolism. *Human Pathology, 3,* 89–95.

Gorlin, R., & Pindborg, J. (1976). *Syndromes of the head and neck.* New York: McGraw-Hill.

Holdsworth, C. E., Endahl, G. L., Soifer, N., Richardson, K. E., & Eyring, E. J. (1973). Comparative biochemical study of otosclerosis and osteogenesis imperfecta. *Archives of Otolaryngology, 98,* 336–339.

Kosoy, J., & Maddox, H. E. (1971). Surgical findings in van de Hoeve's syndrome. *Archives of Otolaryngology, 93,* 115–122.

McKusick, V. A. (1972). *Heritable disorders of connective tissue* (4th ed., pp. 390–454). St. Louis: C. V. Mosby.

Prockop, D. J. (1984). Osteogenesis imperfecta: Phenotypic heterogeneity, protein suicide, short and long collagen. *American Journal of Human Genetics, 36,* 449–505.

Quisling, R. W., Moore, G. R., Jahrsdoerfer, R. A., & Cantrell, R. W. (1979). Osteogenesis imperfecta: A study of 160 family members. *Archives of Otolaryngology, 105,* 207–211.

Riedner, E. D., Levin, S., & Holliday, M. J. (1980). Hearing patterns in dominant osteogenesis imperfecta. *Archives of Otolaryngology, 106,* 737–740.

Sillence, D. P., Senn, A., & Danks, D. M. (1979). Genetic heterogeneity in osteogenesis imperfecta. *Journal of Medical Genetics, 16,* 101–116.

Soifer, N., Weaver, K., Endahl, G. L., & Holdsworth, C. E. (1970). Otosclerosis: A review. *Acta Oto-Laryngologica* (Suppl. 269), 1–25.

Terkildsen, K., Osterhammel, P., & Bretlau, P. (1973). Acoustic middle ear reflexes in patients with otosclerosis. *Archives of Otolaryngology, 98,* 152–155.

Varni, N., & Jaffe, M. (1984). Osteogenesis imperfecta: The basics. *Pediatric Nursing, 10,* 29–33.

Stickler Syndrome
(Progressive Arthro-Ophthalmopathy)

■ Characteristics
Dysmorphology

Hereditary Stickler syndrome was initially described by Stickler and colleagues (1965), with further delination of its wide spectrum by Herrmann, France, Spranger, Opitz, and Wiffler (1975). The anomalies of this syndrome include (see list):

severe myopia

retinal detachment or cataracts

arthropathy, often progressive, similar to juvenile rheumatoid arthritis

musculoskeletal findings of hypotonia, Marfanoid habitus, prominence of ankle, knee, and wrist bones, subluxation of the hip, spondyloepiphyseal dysplasia

Pierre–Robin sequence (micrognathia with cleft palate, submucous cleft or bifid uvula)

mild midfacial hypoplasia

hearing impairment (conductive and sensorineural)

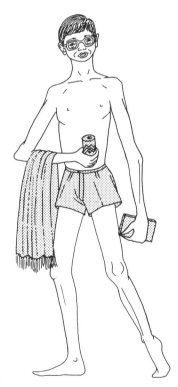

Individuals with Stickler syndrome tend to have long thin extremities with prominence of the ankle, knee, and wrist joints.

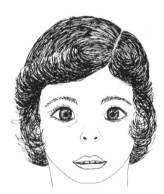

Mild midfacial hypoplasia and microngnathia are features of Stickler syndrome.

The myopia is often severe and requires glasses at an early age.

Depending on the index of suspicion, this condition may be diagnosed at birth because of the Pierre-Robin sequence and a positive
family history of high myopia, childhood arthritis, or cleft palate
(Herrmann et al., 1975). Later presentations are due to ophthalmological or musculoskeletal symptoms. The myopia (8 to 18 diopters)
is usually present before age 10. Joint symptoms are most severe in
hips and knees. Deafness and secondary speech delay may be an
earlier presentation but are relatively uncommon.

Hearing

The external ears are characteristically "low set" with a variety of
auricular malformations reported to occur in approximately 10 to
12 percent of cases. More rarely associated are congenital middle
ear and inner ear anomalies. When middle ear anomalies do occur,
it is predicted that the major involvement will be of malleus and incus because of their origin from the first branchial arch. In severe
cases, multiple middle and inner ear anomalies have been described as basically architectural malformations rather than neural
or end organ developmental anomalies (Igarashi, Filippone, & Alford, 1976).

Bilateral conductive impairment can be expected in the majority of cases, secondary to existing palatal abnormalities. Congenital mixed or sensorineural impairment have been reported to occur with far less frequency. It has been suggested by some (Williams, Williams, Walker, & Bush, 1981), that the incidence of learning impairment is similar to that in cases of isolated cleft palate.

The degree of conductive hearing loss can range from
slight (<15dB) to moderate, with mild conductive hearing loss
most common.

Speech

When patients are identified with Stickler syndrome, those with
oral manifestations are at risk for speech difficulties secondary to
the palatal or oral deficits. At an early age, children may manifest
difficulties with feeding, sucking, and swallowing because of palatal pharyngeal valving problems. Early detection of problems associated with oral-velopharyngeal efficiency should lead to a thorough evaluation of the entire oral pharyngeal system. Submucous
clefts may mask underlying feeding problems that go undetected
until the child develops weight gain problems and secondary side
effects. Surgical intervention to repair the muscle integrity of the
secondary palate should eliminate such problems. Should the
problems be of a less severe nature, the child may perform with
minimum adequacy for deglutitory tasks, but show problems in the
development of speech and language. As with other children with
submucous clefts or overt clefts of the secondary palate, varying

degrees of hypernasality and nasal air emission may accompany attempts to produce simple vowel and consonant elements in the traditional developmental sequence. Failure to develop an oral and nasal contrast in the early years may lead to later articulatory problems, including glottal or pharyngeal substitutions for anterior oral sounds, nasal continuants for oral continuants, and voicing difficulties. With the concomitant conductive hearing loss that often accompanies the clefting condition of the syndrome, problems in language learning may occur. Such difficulties often include listening vocabulary, grammatical difficulties, morphophonemic problems, and expressive differences in terms of length and complexity of the verbal output. With many children with such complex problems, social usage of language is also deficient.

Management

Genetic and Medical

Stickler syndrome is autosomal dominant. As is typical of autosomal dominant conditions, expression is extremely variable, even within the same family. It is estimated that possibly one-half of all Pierre-Robin anomalies may represent the broader arthro-ophthalmopathy syndrome. There is a 50 percent recurrence risk to offspring of affected individuals. The variability in expression makes prediction of severity difficult.

Findings should enable one to exclude Marfan syndrome or other connective tissue problems. Recognition of ophthalmological problems may allow early treatment of retinal detachment and preservation of optimal vision. Preservation of joint function during any period of arthritis is important. This may involve physiotherapy, to retain full range of motion and muscle strength, and the judicious use of anti-inflammatory medications. Joint symptomatology is most frequent from ages 15 to 30, with improvement thereafter.

Hearing

Regular audiometric evaluation is indicated to monitor audiological status closely, as would be indicated for any child with abnormalities of the palate. Assessment of the integrity of the sensorineural system should be performed as early as possible.

Speech

Early speech and language management of this syndrome will focus on problems related to palatal competency. As with other children born with cleft palate, these individuals will need speech and language stimulation by the parents or caregivers. Following surgical management of the cleft condition, speech and language therapy should be instituted. Therapy is designed to focus attention on auditory discrimination of oral and nasal sound contrasts directing the breath stream orally, correct anterior placement of plosive, fricative, and affricative sounds, and emphasis on rate of speech commensurate with articulatory placement abilities. Such direction should lead to a reduction in abnormal articulatory placement and faulty resonance patterns that may develop. Continued evaluation of velopharyngeal competency may be necessary for some patients following a primary surgical procedure. Judgment of resonance balance and objective measurements (nasendoscopy, videofluoroscopy aerodynamics) of velopharygeal competency should be routine if any problems are detected.

Deficits of receptive and oral expressive language should be managed with traditional methods of stimulation, shaping of responses, and emphasis on expanding the child's verbal attempts. Monitoring of hearing sensitivity during the early language learning period is an essential part of the therapy program.

With the later development of visual problems, professionals are encouraged to carefully monitor reading and writing aspects of expressive language, which may suffer because of the ocular deficit. Modified methods of language training may be enhanced with materials suited for the partially sighted. Seeking help from speech educators familiar with the academic difficulties that may be encountered by children with visual problems is encouraged.

Prognosis

Prognosis will depend on severity of manifestation and timing of treatment modalities. Lifespan and intelligence are predicted to follow the distribution in the nonaffected population.

■ References

Herrmann, J., France, T. D., Spranger, J. W., Opitz, J. M., & Wiffler, C. (1975). The Stickler syndrome (hereditary arthroophthalmopathy). *Birth Defects Original Article Series, 11*(2), 76–103.

Igarashi, M., Filippone, M. V., & Alford, B. R. (1976). Temporal bone findings in Pierre-Robin syndrome. *Laryngoscope, 86,* 1679–1687.

Stickler, G. B., Belau, P. G., Farrell, F. J., Jones, J. D., Pugh, D. G., Steinberg, A. G., & Ward, L. E. (1965). Hereditary progressive artho-ophthalmopathy. *Mayo Clinic Proceedings, 40,* 433.

Williams, A. J., Williams, M. A., Walker, C. A., & Bush, P. G. (1981). The Robin anomalad (Pierre-Robin syndrome) — a follow-up story. *Archives of Disease in Childhood, 56,* 663–668.

Treacher Collins Syndrome
(Mandibulofacial Dysostosis, Franceschetti-Zwahlen-Klein Syndrome)

■ Characteristics
Dysmorphology

downward slanting palpebral fissures

coloboma of lower eyelids

malar hypoplasia

mandibular hypoplasia

malformations of the external ear often associated with stenosis or atresia of the auditory canal

hearing impairment

preauricular ear tags

cleft or incompetent soft palate

dental malocclusion and teeth hypoplasia

The well-described Treacher Collins syndrome involves structures derived from the first branchial arch (Collins, 1933). The autosomal dominant nature was then delineated by Franceschetti and Klein (1949). Dysmorphic features include (see list):

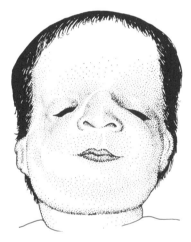

Downward slanting palpebral fissures, coloboma of lower eyelids, malar hypoplasia, mandibular hypoplasia.

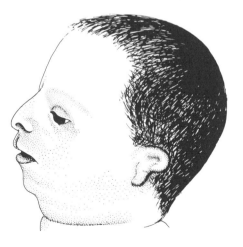

Malformations of the external ear associated with stenosis or atresia of the auditory canal.

Hearing

Pinna malformations occur in approximately 85 percent with approximately one-third of patients having external auditory canal atresia (Stovin, Lyon, & Clemmen, 1960). Widely ranging abnormalities of the external ear have been observed, varying from normal, through minor, abnormalities of the helices to complete microtia. Similarly, the external meatus can range from normal to absent and has been described as characteristically stenotic and sloping upward with a deep pocket superiorly (Maran, 1964). A wide range of tympanic membrane malformations have been reported related to shape, position, and size.

A wide variety of middle ear malformations, with either complete absence of or a poorly developed middle ear cleft, have been described as common (Caldarelli, 1977). Ossicular malformations, including incudomalleal fusion and poorly developed stapes suprastructure, have been reported.

Histopathological studies have documented malformations of the inner ear, including an enlarged cochlear aqueduct and absence of the horizontal canal in more severe forms (Sando, Hemenway, & Morgan, 1968).

A congenital bilateral conductive hearing impairment is most common although presence of sensorineural impairment has been reported in some isolated cases (Hutchinson, Caldarelli, & Valvassori, 1977). Presence of unilateral conductive hearing impairment is unlikely (Maran, 1964).

The degree of hearing loss can range from slight to moderate (<65dB), depending upon the existing form (see Figures 3–4a and 3–4b). Both degree and configuration of hearing loss can vary between ears within given patients (Maran, 1964).

Speech

Deformities that will involve speech and language include underdevelopment of the facial bones, particularly the zygoma and mandible, a high or cleft palate, and abnormal dentition with malocclusion. Although the general appearance of these individuals might suggest that they are mentally retarded, intelligence follows the nonaffected population distribution (Fernandez & Ronis, 1964).

Abnormal position and malocclusion of the teeth is common in this syndrome. The malocclusion may also be associated with severe anterior open bite. Underdevelopment of the mandible results in peculiar curvature of the lower border of the mandible with consequent malocclusion usually involving an open bite that worsens with time.

Cleft palate has been reported to occur in approximately 30 percent of the patients manifesting mandibulofacial dysostosis (Gorlin & Pindborg, 1976). Peterson–Falzone and Pruzansky (1976)

a

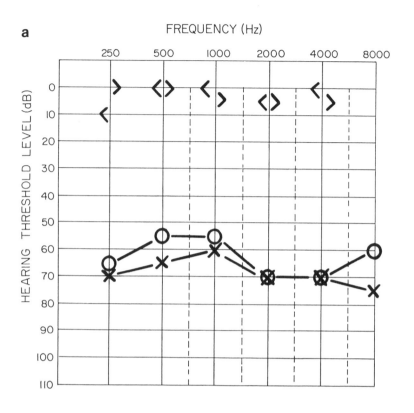

FREQUENCY (Hz)

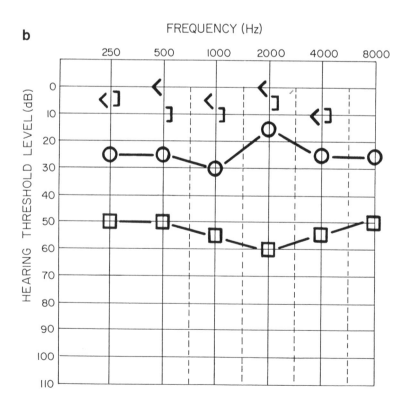

FREQUENCY (Hz)

b

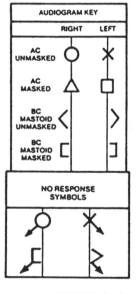

FIGURE 3–4a, b: *Characteristic pure-tone audiometric findings associated with Treacher Collins syndrome.*

reported that congenitally short or immobile palates have been observed both in conjunction with a submucous defect of the hard palate and in the absence of any such defect.

When patients are identified as having Treacher Collins syndrome, usually at birth if the signs are observable, they are at risk for speech and language difficulties related to the oral and aural components of the syndrome. These children may manifest difficulties with sucking, swallowing, and mastication of food. Those with palatopharyngeal valving problems (overt clefts, velopharyngeal incompetence) will be at risk for nasal regurgitation of food and liquid, nasal air emission, hypernasality, and abnormal compensatory articulation problems. Further, language development may be delayed because of the hearing loss of a conductive or mild sensorineural nature. Additionally, some language difficulties may be related to the inability to develop syntactical elements or to form morphophonemic endings related to both oral articulator problems or the hearing loss. Articulation development may be hampered by the severe mandibular underdevelopment and severe open bite and concomitant abnormal tongue posture.

Facial malformations resulting from this condition vary in severity from mild to severe. As the severity of the disorder increases, the expectations are that articulation will be more severely affected. Likewise, articulation and language deficits will be affected by the severity and type of the hearing loss (conductive versus sensorineural). Intermittancy of the hearing loss may cause problems in linguistic development if it exists at critical learning periods.

Management

Genetics and Medical

This condition follows an autosomal dominant pattern. The gene may be either inherited or the result of a spontaneous mutation. Care should be given to close examination of parents, as wide variability of expression of this gene may manifest as very mild or partial clinical features (see Figures 3–5, 3–6, 3–7, & 3–8). This should not be confused with Goldenhar (oculoauriculovertebral) syndrome or acrofacial dysostosis.

Hearing

Management strategies include surgical reconstruction of the outer ear, early intervention with amplification, typically in the form of a bone conduction hearing aid (Sortini, 1981), and a speech and language program. With adequate amplification, severe language comprehension deficits can be avoided. Parents of infants and preschool aged children can usually conduct effective aural rehabilitation programs under the guidance of a skilled professional and most

FIGURE 3–5: *A family in which the gene for Treacher Collins syndrome demonstrates extremely variable expression. The mother has two sons, with the youngest demonstrating moderately severe signs of Treacher Collins syndrome.*

can be expected to follow a regular school program from kindergarten on, providing they receive sufficient support services in speech, hearing, and language development.

Speech

Two types of surgical management may be expected to facilitate development of speech and language. As with any child with a palatal cleft, primary palatoplasty is the procedure of choice to normalize the oral, nasal, and pharyngeal area for aid in developing swallowing and speech activities. There remains the possibility, following

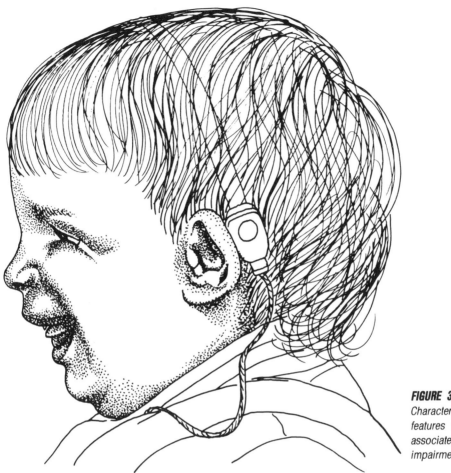

FIGURE 3-6: *Characteristic facial features with associated hearing impairment.*

primary palatoplasty, that a secondary procedure will be required to augment the soft palate area should it be found incompetent as the child ages. A palatopharyngoplasty (pharyngeal flap) is the method of choice here. Certain children may not be candidates for primary or secondary surgical procedures because of tissue deficiencies, and systemic or neurological damage. These children should be managed with prosthetic techniques designed to separate the oral and nasal cavities and provide a basis for normal swallowing and speech development. Surgical or prosthetic management of these individuals is not without problems caused by their altered anatomy. Peterson-Falzone and Pruzansky (1976) reported that physical management of the velopharyngeal port may be unsuccessful for a number of reasons. The nasopharynx may be inaccessible due to restricted oral opening resulting from hypoplasia of the mandible. Constriction of the airway may complicate anesthesia. The narrow and anomalous shape of the nasopharynx and palatal vault may further complicate the fitting of a prosthesis. Further, a

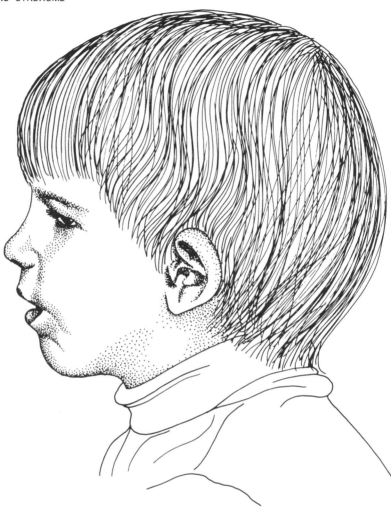

FIGURE 3-7:
Mild changes of ear morphology with minimal mandibular and malar hypoplasia.

prosthesis may have to work against the dead weight of the velum. The prosthesis may also affect already disordered dentition.

The second physical management technique involves surgical alteration of the maxilla or mandible (osteotomy). These surgical procedures are designed to normalize jaw relationships and provide an oral environment for better speech production and manipulation of food. These procedures are usually completed in adolescence in order that facial growth is not restricted by alteration of growth centers. Based on published reports, such a procedure may be expected to facilitate improvements in articulation, particularly fricative and affricative sounds (Glass, Knapp, & Bloomer, 1977; Witzel, Ross, & Munro, 1980). In addition, modification of open bite and concomitant tongue posture may be expected to facilitate improvements in production of bilabial, labiodental, and linguo-alveolar sounds.

For many of these children, speech and language stimulation in the early years is critical. Interaction between the audiologist,

FIGURE 3–8:
An obligate carrier of the Treacher Collins syndrome gene with extremely mild manifestations.

otolaryngologist, and speech pathologist is crucial, as these individuals will encounter a combination of audiologic and orofacial anomalies. It should be expected that speech therapy will be necessary in order to correct disordered speech production resulting from the abnormal size and shape of the speech production mechanism. Likewise, attention must be paid to resonance imbalance arising from a defective oral and nasal valve. In severe cases, speech therapy is usually not initiated until the palatopharyngeal valve is normalized.

Prognosis

Intelligence is usually normal, but developmental delays due to hearing loss or speech problems may be encountered. According to

Sataloff (1983), surgical treatment can be extremely successful in carefully selected cases. Response to amplification can be excellent in conjunction with an appropriately designed acoustic and auditory management program. Prognosis will necessarily depend on severity and success of surgical and behavior management techniques. As is the case with any condition involving auditory or oral defects, the earlier that management begins, the better the prognosis.

■ References

Caldarelli, D. (1977). Congenital middle ear anomalies associated with craniofacial and skeletal syndromes. In B. F. Jaffee (Ed.), *Hearing loss in children* (pp. 310–340). Baltimore: University Park Press.

Collins, E. T. (1933). Cases with symmetrical congenital notches in the outer part of each lower lid and defective development of the malar bones. *Transactions of the Ophthalmological Society of the United Kingdom, 20,* 190–192.

Fernandez, A. C., & Ronis, M. L. (1964). The Treacher–Collins syndrome. *Archives of Otolaryngology, 80,* 505–520.

Franceschetti, A., & Klein, D. (1949). Mandibulo-facial dysostosis: New hereditary syndrome. *Acta Ophthalmologica, 27,* 143–224.

Glass, L., Knapp, J., & Bloomer, H. (1977). Speech and lingual behaviour before and after mandibular osteotomy. *Journal of Oral Surgery, 35,* 104–109.

Gorlin, R., & Pindborg, J. (1976). *Syndromes of the head and neck* (pp. 453–457). New York: McGraw-Hill.

Hutchinson, J., Caldarelli, D., & Valvassori, G. (1977). The otologic manifestations of mandibulofacial dysostosis. *Transactions of the American Academy of Ophthalomology and Otolaryngology, 84,* 520–528.

Maran, A. (1964). The Treacher Collins syndrome. *Journal of Laryngology, 78,* 135–151.

Peterson–Falzone, S., & Pruzansky, S. (1976). Cleft palate and congenital palatopharyngeal incompetency in mandibulofacial dysostosis: Frequency and problems in treatment. *Cleft Palate Journal, 13,* 354–360.

Sando, I., Hemenway, W., & Morgan, W. (1968). Histopathology of the temporal bones in mandibulofacial dysostosis. *Transactions of the American Academy of Ophthalmology and Otolaryngology, 72,* 913–924.

Sataloff, R. (1983). Hearing loss associated with hereditary diseases and syndromes. *Ear, Nose and Throat Journal, 62,* 571–593.

Sortini, A. (1981). Hearing aids for children with bilateral congenital ear canal atresia. *Hearing Instruments, 32,* 20–22.

Stovin, J., Lyon, J., & Clemmen, R. (1960). Mandibulofacial dysostosis. *Radiology, 74,* 225–231.

Witzel, M., Ross, R., & Munro, I. (1980). Articulation before and after facial osteotomy. *Journal of Maxillofacial Surgery, 8,* 161–256.

Van Der Woude Syndrome
(Cleft Lip or Palate and Lip Pits; Lip Pit Syndrome)

■ Characteristics
Dysmorphology

lower lip pits (representing fistulas from mucous cysts)

cleft lip with or without cleft palate

hypodontia (especially second premolars)

Family studies by van der Woude in 1954 documented affected individuals from multiple generations who demonstrated some or all of the findings of (see list):

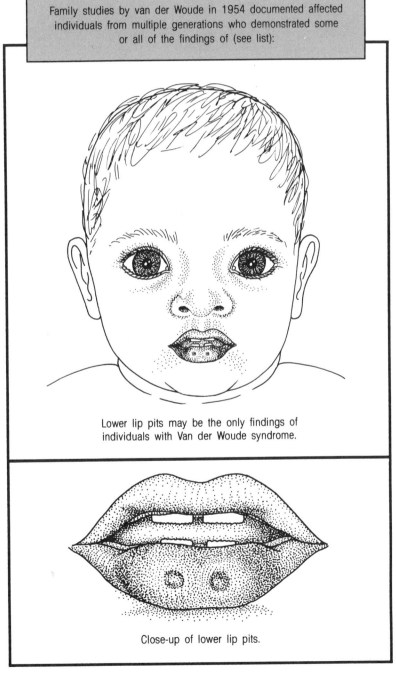

Lower lip pits may be the only findings of individuals with Van der Woude syndrome.

Close-up of lower lip pits.

Isolated lip pits are the most common minimal finding. The fistulas may secrete a mucoid discharge from underlying accessory salivary glands and mucous cysts. Clefting may not be present in all individuals with this syndrome, but is the most common presenting sign of this condition.

Hearing

Although van der Woude syndrome is not characterized by a hearing impairment *per se,* it should be noted that there is a high incidence of conductive hearing loss among individuals with a cleft palate (Siedentop, 1977). The deficiency of the palate musculature causes poor Eustachian tube function, which may cause inadequate middle ear ventilation, effusion of fluid, tympanic membrane retraction, and hearing loss (Bluestone & Shurin, 1974). The incidence of significant pathologic middle ear changes in children with cleft palate is 90 percent for children less than one year of age, 30 percent in preschoolers, and 10 percent in children of school age (Siedentop, 1977). Ninety percent of children with overt cleft palates suffer from recurrent otitis media (Graham, 1963; Holborow, 1962; Paradise & Bluestone, 1969; Stool & Randall, 1967). The incidence of recurrent or chronic middle ear disease among children with submucous cleft palate was reported to be 39 percent.

Conductive hearing loss associated with a variety of causes ranging from recurrent or chronic otitis media to cholesteatoma has been reported among children with submucous cleft palate. It is also expected that a considerable number of children will also display either a sensorineural or a mixed hearing loss (Bergstrom & Hemenway, 1971). Conductive hearing loss is most prominent among children between 3 and 8 years of age (Bennett, Ward, & Tait, 1968; Halfond & Ballenger, 1956; Jarvis, 1976). The degree of hearing loss can range from slight to moderate, depending on the cause and extent of the conductive hearing impairment.

Speech

Cervenka, Gorlin, and Anderson (1967) observed lip pits in about 70 percent of those individuals who carry the gene, and orofacial clefting in 39 percent of people demonstrating the gene. Of the congenital lip pit cases analyzed by Cervenka and colleagues (1967), 65 percent were in female subjects. This, however, may reflect the fact that more women are apt to seek cosmetic surgical relief of the condition. The lip pits are usually bilateral and symmetrically placed on the vermilion of the lower lip. Other less common variations include asymmetrical single pit, central single pit, or pits of the upper lip (Gorlin & Pindborg, 1964). Of those having lip pits, about 70 percent may have cleft of the lip with or without palate (Gorlin & Pindborg, 1964). Approximately 0.5 percent of individuals with cleft lip with or without cleft palate have lip pits (van der Woude, 1954). In addition, Glass, Stewart, and Miles (1979) have noted that a submucous cleft of the palate may also be associated with lip pits.

The lip pits as a single observable entity should not produce significant speech defects. In severe cases, bilabial and labiodental consonant sounds (e.g., /p/, /b/, /m/, /f/, /v/) may be affected, producing cosmetic and acoustic-perceptual alterations of correct sound output. Cleft palate associated with the condition will produce similar acoustic, aerodynamic, and perceptual defects of speech sound production as seen with other syndromes, namely, hypernasality, nasal air emission, and sound substitutions, distortions, and omissions. In early childhood, problems with sucking, swallowing, and feeding may also be present. Severity of the condition will determine the number and extent of these problems.

There are no published data concerning the severity of the disorder relating to speech and language difficulties. Further research is needed to determine speech and language characteristics associated with different levels of expressivity.

Management

Genetics and Medical

Van der Woude syndrome is autosomal dominant with variable expression and reduced penetrance (approximately 80 percent). A careful family history and examination is needed to document this condition. Clinically, it is important to differentiate from isolated cleft lip with or without palate, and other clefting syndromes, as recurrence risks will vary considerably. An affected individual or obligate carrier, as determined by pedigree analysis, has a 50 percent chance of passing the gene for this trait to any offspring. This syndrome's features can be seen as part of more generalized multisystem syndromes such as the popliteal pterygium and oral-facial-digital type I syndromes.

Hearing

Myringotomy and tympanotomy tube insertion should be performed within the first six months if possible (Paradise, 1980). Moreover, it is recommended that the physicians should repeat the myringotomy and tubes if necessary to keep the infant's ears clear and hearing normal. Hearing should be monitored on a regular basis with close medical follow-up when necessary (Northern & Downs, 1984). Mild to moderate power hearing aids may be in order for children who do not respond well to medical treatment (Ling & Ling, 1978; Northern & Downs, 1984).

Speech

When a cleft of the soft or hard palate exists, surgical techniques designed to obturate the cleft condition may be instituted. Severity of the cleft condition will determine which palatoplasty or pharyngoplasty may be performed. In general, the earlier the palatal area is "normalized," the more optimal will be the mechanism for the development of speech and language. In addition, conductive hearing problems may be reduced with surgical management of the cleft. Behavioral management of the speech and language difficulties that exist should follow developmental guidelines for speech sound and linguistic function. Depending upon the severity of the lip pits, surgical correction of the mucosa should produce a cosmetic improvement in the condition. Reduction in the unevenness of the lip area may also provide better range of motion for functional closure for bilabial and labiodental speech sound production. Traditional speech therapy may be needed to aid the child in altering lip position for the best sound production. Surgical removal of the fistula is sometimes desirable to control the mucoid secretions.

Prognosis

Prognosis will depend on the presence, severity, and management of the oral cleft. Where applicable, the prognosis will depend on the expressivity and severity of the lip pits and cleft of the palate. Given the success of modern surgical and behavioral management techniques, the individuals with this syndrome should have a rate of success similar to that of other persons with lip or palatal defects.

The incidence and severity of middle ear problems related to cleft palates decrease as children grow older (Goetzinger, Embrey, & Brooks, 1960; Graham, 1963; Siedentop, 1977).

■ References

Bennett, M., Ward, P. H., & Tait, C. A. (1968). Otologic-audiologic study of cleft palate children. *Laryngoscope, 78,* 1011–1019.

Bergstrom, L., & Hemenway, W. G. (1971). Otologic problems in submucous cleft palate. *Southern Medical Journal, 64,* 1172–1177.

Bluestone, C. D., & Shurin, P. A. (1974). Middle ear disease in children: Pathogenesis, diagnosis and management. *Pediatric Clinics of North America, 21,* 379–400.

Cervenka, J., Gorlin, R. J., & Anderson, V. E. (1967). The syndrome of pits of the lower lip and cleft lip and/or palate. Genetic considerations. *American Journal of Human Genetics, 19,* 416–432.

Glass, L., Stewart, R., & Miles, J. (1979). The speech-language pathologist's role in understanding the genetics of van der Woude's syndrome. *Journal of Speech and Hearing Disorders, 44,* 472–478.

Goetzinger, C. P., Embrey, J. E., & Brooks, R. (1960). Auditory assessment of cleft palate adults. *Acta Otolaryngology (Stockholm), 52,* 551–557.

Gorlin, R., & Pindborg, J. (1964). *Syndromes of the head and neck.* New York: McGraw-Hill.

Graham, M. D. (1963). A longitudinal study of ear disease and hearing loss in parents with cleft lips and palates. *Transactions of the American Academy of Ophthalmology and Otolaryngology, 67,* 213–222.

Halfond, M. M., & Ballenger, J. J. (1956). An audiological and otolaryngologic study of cleft lip and cleft palate cases. *Archives of Otolaryngology, 64,* 58–62.

Holborow, C. A. (1962). Deafness associated with cleft palate. *Laryngoscope, 76,* 762–773.

Jarvis, J. F. (1976). Audiological status of children with cleft palate: A review of 350 cases. *Audiology, 15,* 242–248.

Ling, D., & Ling, A. H. (1978). *Aural habilitation.* Washington, DC: A. G. Bell Association.

Northern, J. L., & Downs, M. P. (Eds.). (1984). *Hearing in children (3rd ed.).* Baltimore: Williams & Wilkins.

Paradise, J. L. (1980). Otitis media in infants and children. *Pediatrics, 65,* 917–943.

Paradise, J. L., & Bluestone, C. D. (1969). Diagnosis and management of ear disease in cleft palate children. *American Academy of Ophthalmology and Otolaryngology, 73,* 709–714.

Siedentop, K. H. (1977). Eustachian tube function. In B. F. Jaffe (Ed.), *Hearing loss in children: A comprehensive text* (pp. 381–396). Baltimore: University Park Press.

Stool, S., & Randall, P. (1967). Unexpected ear disease in infants with cleft palate. *Cleft Palate Journal, 4,* 99–103.

van der Woude, A. (1954). Fistula labii inferioris congenita and its association with cleft lip and palate. *American Journal of Human Genetics, 6,* 224–256.

Waardenburg Syndrome

■ Characteristics
Dysmorphology

*lateral displacement
of the inner canthi*

*pigmentary disturbances
(white forelock, heterochromia
irides, vitiligo)*

*sensorineural hearing
impairment*

broad and high nasal bridge

medial flare of eyebrows

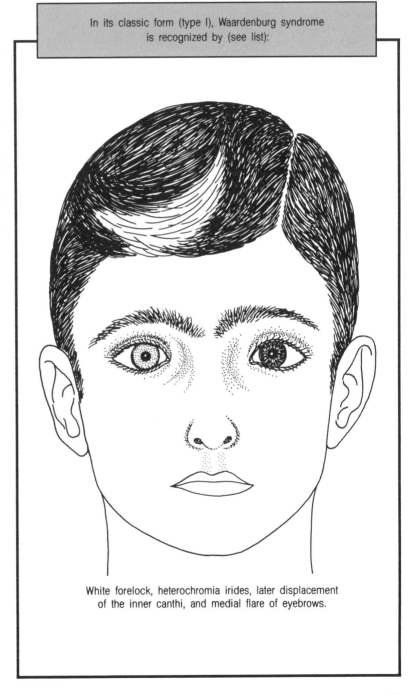

In its classic form (type I), Waardenburg syndrome
is recognized by (see list):

White forelock, heterochromia irides, later displacement
of the inner canthi, and medial flare of eyebrows.

Type II is said not to have lateral displacement of the canthi, but is associated with a higher percentage of hearing impairment (50 percent in type II versus 25 percent in type I). The white forelock may be present at birth and then become pigmented later.

Hearing

A variety of inner ear anomalies have been identified and described. Findings of histological and tomographic studies include: complete absence or malformation of the organ of Corti, atrophy of the spiral ganglion and stria vascularis, and a paucity of cochlear neurons (Fisch, 1959; Marcus, 1968).

Congenital bilateral and unilateral sensorineural impairment is associated with and is the most serious expression of this syndrome. Congenital sensorineural impairment occurs in approximately 25 percent of type I cases and in approximately 50 percent of type II cases. As mentioned previously, the hearing impairment is most common in type II.

The degree of sensorineural hearing loss associated with Waardenburg syndrome can range from mild to profound (see Figure 3–9a, b, c). Three different audiometric profiles that have been described include (1) profound bilateral sensorineural hearing loss with only minimal response to low frequency acoustic and vibratory stimuli, (2) moderate to severe bilateral sensorineural hearing loss with a rising audiometric configuration, and (3) profound unilateral sensorineural hearing loss. A progressive loss of hearing sensitivity has been reported in isolated cases.

Speech

There are less common facial features that may involve speech and language. These include cleft lip or palate, a prognathic mandible (Goodman & Gorlin, 1977), and a full and protruding lower lip (Gorlin & Pindborg, 1964; Goodman & Gorlin, 1977).

In cases where a cleft of the palate is evident, the typical cleft related problems may be expected. These include problems in childhood with sucking, swallowing, nasal regurgitation, nasal air emission, hypernasality, and the potential for abnormal compensatory articulations. In cases where a prognathic mandible is evident, one may see and hear oral distortions of sibilants, fricatives, and affricatives, related to the abnormal tongue-mandible-maxilla relationship (Peterson, 1972). The presence of a full or protruding lower lip may place some individuals at risk for difficulties with bilabial and labiodental sound production. The more frequent occurrence of a sensorineural hearing loss may be expected to affect language development.

There are no published data that refer to the range of severity of speech and language manifestations of this syndrome. The

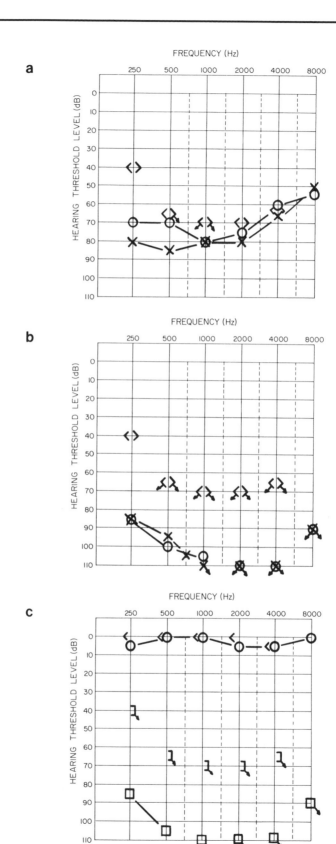

FIGURE 3-9a, b, c: Characteristic pure-tone audiometric findings associated with Waardenburg syndrome.

greater the severity of the disorder, the more profound the effect on articulation and language.

Management

Genetics and Medical

Waardenburg syndrome is an autosomal dominant condition with variable penetrance and expression. Advanced paternal age has been associated with sporadic cases (new mutations). An affected individual is at a 50 percent risk for passing the trait on to each child.

Hearing

Management should include early intervention with amplification and a comprehensive habilitative management program appropriate to congenital sensorineural hearing loss impairment. Careful audiometric monitoring should be included to document any change in auditory status and to modify the habilitation program accordingly.

Speech

If a palatal cleft is present, primary palatoplasty may be performed to normalized the oral-nasal-pharyngeal area for aid in developing swallowing and speech activities. A pharyngeal flap procedure may also be required to augment the soft palate region. Prosthetic techniques may be used in lieu of surgery to achieve the same goals. If the mandible is severely prognathic, a mandibular osteotomy may be considered in order to bring the mandible back into a more appropriate relationship with the maxilla.

   In cases where the speech production mechanism is significantly abnormal (e.g., cleft palate, prognathic mandible), speech therapy may be directed toward improving articulation and oral and nasal resonance balance. It appears more likely that, in this syndrome, one must attend to speech or language difficulties associated with the sensorineural hearing loss.

Prognosis

Life expectancy for individuals with Waardenburg syndrome is normal. Assuming that an appropriate habilitation program is instituted early, speech and language development can be expected to be roughly proportional to the severity of the audiological status.

   Where applicable, prognosis will depend on the severity and success of surgical and behavioral management techniques. Given the more commonly occurring auditory deficits, prognosis should be expected to be higher if management begins early.

■ References

Fisch, L. (1959). Deafness as part of a hereditary syndrome. *Journal of Laryngology, 73,* 355–383.

Goodman, R., & Gorlin, R. (1977). *Atlas of the face in genetic disorders.* St. Louis: C. V. Mosby.

Gorlin, R., & Pindborg, J. (1964). *Syndromes of the head and neck.* New York: McGraw-Hill.

Marcus, R. E. (1968). Vestibular function and additional findings in Waardenburg's syndrome. *Acta Otolaryngolotica (Stockholm), 229,* 1–30.

Peterson, S. (1972). Speech pathology in craniofacial malformations other than cleft lip and palate. *ASHA Reports, 8,* 111–113.

Jervell and Lange-Nielsen Syndrome

(Cardioauditory Syndrome; Deafness and Functional Heart Disease; Surdicardiac Syndrome)

■ Characteristics
Dysmorphology

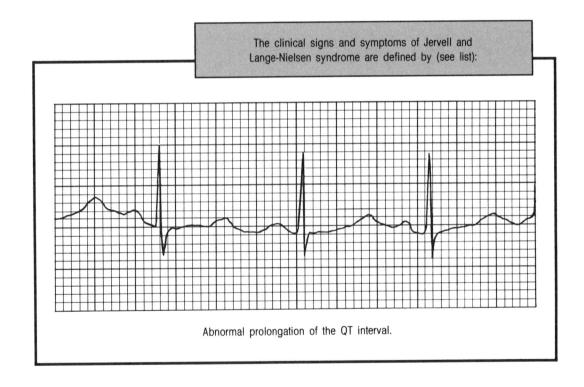

The clinical signs and symptoms of Jervell and Lange-Nielsen syndrome are defined by (see list):

Abnormal prolongation of the QT interval.

profound congenital deafness

cardiac conduction defect characterized by a prolonged Q-T

interval and large upright, inverted, or biphasic T-waves

syncopal (fainting) attacks secondary to cardiac irregularities

occasional death during syncopal attacks (probably due to ventricular fibrillation)

In Jervell and Lange-Nielsen's (1975) report, four affected sibs out of six lent support to an autosomal recessive etiology. Fraser, Froggatt and Murphy (1964) calculated the prevalence of this condition in Great Britain to be between 1.6 and 6 per million. They also suggested that heterozygous carriers of this gene might show subtle disturbances of the Q-T interval on electrocardiogram examination.

Hearing

Histopathological investigations of temporal bones from individuals with the Jervell and Lange-Nielsen syndrome revealed the presence of PAS (periodic acid–Schiff) positive hyaline nodules throughout both the cochlea and vestibular portions of the membranous labyrinth close to the terminal vessels of the stria vascularis (Friedmann, Fraser, & Froggatt, 1966). Widespread degeneration of the sensory end organs of the cochlea and of the vestibular apparatus were also reported. In the degenerated organ of Corti, the tectorial membrane is altered (i.e., shrunken or retracted). Also, Reissner's membrane is collapsed and adherent to the stria vascularis, the tectorial membrane, or the ramparts of the organ of Corti (Friedmann et al., 1966).

Jervell and Lange-Nielsen syndrome is characterized by a congenital sensorineural hearing loss, bilaterally. The audiogram typically displays a severe or profound hearing loss at higher audiometric frequencies.

Speech

The speech language problems that occur with this syndrome are secondary to deafness and will therefore vary essentially according to hearing levels. Special educational treatment should include speech development procedures of the type normally provided for children who are hearing impaired. As with all such cases, the best results are to be obtained if spoken language is developed from early infancy through effective parent and infant work that integrates audiology, speech and language pathology, and educational support services for the family (Ling & Ling, 1978).

Management

Genetics and Medical

This is a well-documented autosomal recessive condition. The presence of a positive family history of consanguinity may also be helpful in differentiating this condition from other forms of acquired

Q-T prolongation. The Ward-Romano syndrome, an autosomal dominant condition affecting cardiac conduction, also needs to be ruled out. When the diagnostic criteria are satisfied, parents of an affected child may be counseled regarding a 25 percent recurrence risk in future children.

The detection of children with Jervell and Lange-Nielsen syndrome is extremely important. Thus, an electrocardiogram should be part of the medical evaluation of individuals with a severe or profound congenital sensorineural hearing loss who experience seizures and syncope. Also, as there is the possibility that children with severe profound congenital hearing loss will have the Jervell and Lange-Nielsen syndrome, professionals who work with hearing impaired children should be trained in cardiopulmonary resuscitation (Wahl & Macdonald–Dick II, 1980).

The management of heart rhythm irregularities should include especially careful cardiology consultation to avoid dangerous syncopal attacks or sudden death. Propranolol is considered the drug of choice to control the arrhythmias, ventricular tachycardia, or vestibular fibrillation associated with the Jervell and Lange-Nielsen syndrome (Moss & Schwartz, 1979; Raine & Pichering, 1977). Left stellectomy (surgical removal of the left stellate ganglion and its nerves to the heart) has been proposed as an alternative method of treatment. However, this surgical approach is still considered experimental (Wahl & Macdonald–Dick II, 1980). An automatic implantable defibrillation device has also been used with success in patients with ventricular arrhythmias secondary to the prolonged Q-T interval (Mirowski, Reid, Mower, et al., 1980).

Hearing

Children with the Jervell and Lange-Nielsen syndrome should be fitted with appropriate hearing aids as soon as possible. Also, these children should participate in a preschool aural rehabilitation program. Specialized education programs for children who are hearing impaired will likely be required.

Prognosis

Until recently, approximately one-half of the patients with the Jervell and Lange-Nielsen syndrome died before age 15. Only a few individuals survived past age 21. However, since the introduction of the drug propranolol to treat the characteristic heart irregularities, Schwartz and Periti (1975) have reported that mortality due to the disease has been reduced to less than 6 percent. Audiologically, there is little progression of hearing loss over the years.

■ References

Fraser, G. R., Froggatt, P., & Murphy, T. (1964). Genetical aspects of the cardio-auditory syndrome of Jervell and Lange-Nielsen (congenital deafness and electrocardiographic abnormalities). *Annals of Human Genetics, (London), 28,* 133–155.

Friedmann, I., Fraser, G. R., & Froggatt, P. (1966). Pathology of the ear in the cardioauditory syndrome of Jervell and Lange-Nielsen (Recessive deafness with electrocardiographic abnormalities). *Journal of Laryngology and Otology, 80,* 451–470.

Jervell, A., & Lange-Nielsen, F. (1957). Congenital deaf-mutism, functional heart disease with prolongation of the QT interval, and sudden death. *American Heart Journal, 54,* 59–68.

Ling, D., & Ling, A. H. (1978). *Aural habilitation.* Washington, DC: A. G. Bell Association.

Mirowski, M., Reid, P. R., Mower, M. N., et al. (1980). Termination of malignant ventricular arrhythmias with an implanted automatic defibrillator in human beings. *The New England Journal of Medicine, 303,* 322–324.

Moss, A. J., & Schwartz, P. J. (1979). Sudden death and the idiopathic long Q-T syndromes. *American Journal of Medicine, 66,* 6–20.

Raine, A. E. G., & Pichering, T. G. (1977). Cardiovascular and sympathetic response to exercise after long-term beta-adrenergic blockade. *British Medical Journal, 2,* 90–92.

Schwartz, P. J., Periti, M., & Malliani, A. (1975). The long Q-T syndrome. *The American Heart Journal, 89,* 378–390.

Wahl, R. A., & Macdonald-Dick, M. II. (1980). Congenital deafness with cardiac arrhythmias: The Jervell and Lange-Nielsen syndrome. *American Annals of the Deaf, 125,* 34–37.

Laurence-Moon-Biedl Syndrome
(Bardet-Biedl Syndrome;
Laurence-Moon-Biedl-Bardet Syndrome)

■ Characteristics
Dysmorphology

polydactyly

retinitis pigmentosa

hypogonadism

obesity

mental deficiency

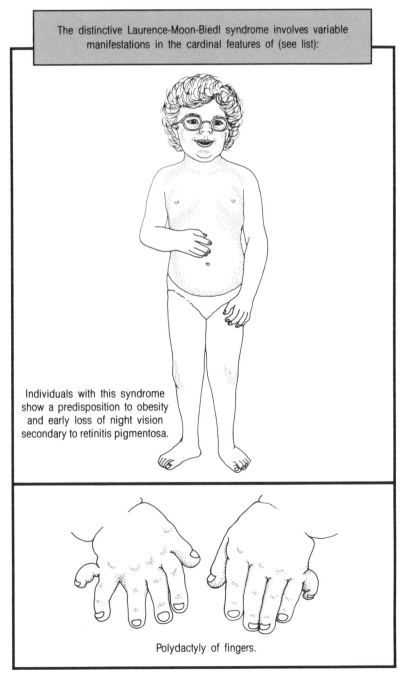

The distinctive Laurence-Moon-Biedl syndrome involves variable manifestations in the cardinal features of (see list):

Individuals with this syndrome show a predisposition to obesity and early loss of night vision secondary to retinitis pigmentosa.

Polydactyly of fingers.

Polydactyly may be observed at birth, but the lack of other findings makes early diagnosis difficult. Obesity and developmental delay become more apparent in later childhood. In a review of 214 cases reported since 1959, Schachat and Maumenee (1982) found mild to moderate mental retardation in 85 percent of cases. Although there may be associated neurological symptoms such as seizures, cranial nerve palsies, or ataxia, there is no characteristic neuropathology demonstrable. The deterioration of retinal function may initially be evident as difficulty in seeing in darkness or low light situations.

Objective testing may reveal loss of central and/or peripheral vision. Hypogonadism is easier diagnosed in male patients, as external genitalia may be smaller and associated with cryptorchidism or hypospadias. Less commonly observed problems include endocrine disturbances, congenital heart disease, and renal defects.

Hearing

Hearing impairment is thought to be rare among those with Laurence-Moon-Biedl syndrome, although an accurate estimate of the incidence in affected individuals has yet to be determined. In a review of 611 cases with Laurence-Moon-Biedl syndrome, Burn (1950) identified a total of 10 (1.63 percent) as having "deaf-mutism." The literature suggests that the hearing impairment associated with Laurence-Moon-Biedl syndrome is sensorineural in nature and progressive, with its onset characteristically occurring during late childhood (Konigsmark & Gorlin, 1976).

Speech

Patients with this syndrome have been reported to demonstrate language problems. Descriptions include slow speech and language development (Ciccarelli & Vesell, 1961), scanning speech (Roth, 1947), difficult speech with tongue deviations (Burn, 1950), and delayed speech (Serejski, 1929). Structural deviations reported in the literature include bifid uvula (Baldi, 1945) and high arched palate (Blumel & Knicker, 1959). A more detailed investigation of the speech and language characteristics of this population was conducted by Garstecki, Borton, Stark, and Kennedy (1972). The three subjects studied demonstrated articulation errors, oral motor control difficulties, hypernasality, breathy voice, retarded language development, mental retardation, and conductive hearing loss.

The variables of mental retardation, hearing loss, and neuromuscular involvement appear most important to function from a speech perspective. Speech and language development and school performance could be adversely affected by the presence of intellectual handicap. Oral motor control difficulties may also be expected to contribute significantly to problems in this area.

Management

Genetics and Medical

The Laurence-Moon-Biedl syndrome is autosomal recessive in nature. Parents of an affected child have as high as a 25 percent recurrence risk in any subsequent pregnancy. However, before this counseling is offered, it is necessary to obtain a detailed family history to rule out other pattens of inheritance. There is also controversy as to the degree of heterogeneity that exists. The patients initially reported by Laurence and Moon (1865) lacked polydactyly and had spastic paraplegia. Those patients represent a distinct syndrome from the one that now carries the designation of the Laurence-Moon-Biedl syndrome (Solis–Cohen & Weiss, 1925).

When the Laurence-Moon-Biedl syndrome is suspected from the presence of cardinal features, further evaluation of cardiac and renal status is indicated. In the absence of any structural anomalies delineated, annual follow-up of renal and ophthalmological function is still recommended, as problems may develop with time. A urinalysis can indicate problems with renal glomerular function. Early detection of renal or eye signs open potential avenues of preventative treatment.

Hearing

With the possibility of late onset or progressive hearing impairment, routine audiological assessments should be scheduled on an annual basis.

Speech

Given the prevalence of mental retardation, it is important to diagnose and begin treatment of speech and language in this population as early as possible. Input from speech and language pathologist, special educators, audiologists, and aural rehabilitation specialists sould be utilized in an effort to optimize speech and language development. Although not given extensive attention in previous literature, Garstecki and colleagues (1972) attributed significant speech and language difficulties to, at least in part, neuromuscular deviations. This variable should be addressed both in the diagnosis and treatment of patients with this syndrome.

Prognosis

The variability of expression in this disorder makes it difficult to generalize regarding prognosis. Each person needs individualized attention to ongoing management and treatment.

■ References

Baldi, E. (1945). Sindrome de Laurence-Moon-Biedl [Laurence-Moon-Biedl syndrome]. *Obstetrica y Ginecologia Latino-Americanas, 3,* 619–632.

Blumel, J., & Knicker, W. (1959). Laurence-Moon-Bardet-Biedl syndrome: Review of the literature and a report of five cases including a family group with three affected males. *Texas Reports on Biology and Medicine, 17,* 391–410.

Burn, R. (1950). Deafness and the Laurence-Moon-Biedl syndrome. *British Journal of Ophthalmology, 34,* 65–88.

Ciccarelli, E., & Vesell, E. (1961). Laurence-Moon-Biedl syndrome: Report of an unusual family. *American Journal of Diseases of Children, 101,* 519–524.

Garstecki, D., Borton, T., Stark, E., & Kennedy, B. (1972). Speech, language, and hearing problems in the Laurence-Moon-Biedl syndrome. *Journal of Speech and Hearing Disorders, 37,* 407–413.

Konigsmark, B. W., & Gorlin, R. J. (1976). *Genetic and metabolic deafness.* Toronto: W. B. Saunders.

Laurence, J. Z., & Moon, R. C. (1865). Four cases of "retinitis pigmentosa," occurring in the same family, and accompanied by general imperfections of development. *Ophthalmology Reviews, 2,* 32.

Roth, A. (1947). Familial eunuchoidism: The Laurence-Moon-Biedl syndrome. *Journal of Urology, 57,* 427–445.

Schachat, A., & Maumenee, I. (1982). Bardet-Biedl syndrome and related disorders. *Archives of Ophthalmology, 100,* 285–288.

Serejski, M. (1929). Biedlsche krankheit. *Medizinische Klinik, 25,* 1620–1622.

Solis–Cohen, S., & Weiss, E. (1925). Dystrophia adiposogenitalis with atypical retinitis pigmentosa and mental deficiency: The Laurence-Biedl syndrome. *American Journal of Medical Science, 169,* 489–505.

Mucopolysaccharidoses Syndromes

■ Characteristics

The mucopolysaccharidoses (MPS) syndromes are a heterogeneous group of disorders characterized by excessive storage of mucopolysaccharides (complex carbohydrates) in various body tissue and organs. Depending on the enzyme deficiency, different clinical presentations result. Table 3–1 (see next page) lists the MPS conditions reviewed by Spranger (1983).

It should be stressed that there exists tremendous clinical variability between the MPS syndromes. Some may be very mild or asymptomatic. What follows are brief summaries of dysmorphologies and current knowledge regarding speech and hearing characteristics of select MPS syndromes.

MPS 1-H severe Hurler syndrome, demonstrating coarsening of the facial features and unruly hair secondary to disturbed central nervous system development.

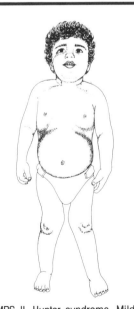

MPS II, Hunter syndrome. Milder clinical course than in Hurler syndrome. Abdomen enlarged secondary to hepatosplenomegaly and evidence of dysostosis multiplex.

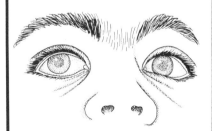

Corneas clouding commonly seen in MPS 1-H.

TABLE 3–1.
Mucopolysaccharidoses Syndromes.

Type	Eponym	Genetics
MPS I-H	Hurler	Autosomal recessive
MPS I-S	Scheie	Autosomal recessive
MPS II	Hunter	X-linked recessive
MPS III	Sanfilippo	Autosomal recessive
MPS IV	Morquio	Autosomal recessive
MPS V	Now MPS I-S	
MPS VI	Maroteaux-Lamy	Autosomal recessive
MPS VII	Sly	Autosomal recessive

Hurler Syndrome (MPS I-H)

Individuals with Hurler syndrome appear normal at birth, with clinical features becoming more apparent with age. Clinical manifestations include:

- progressive mental deterioration
- coarsening of facial features
- clouding of the corneas
- organomegaly
- skeletal dysplasia with joint contractures
- inguinal hernias
- thick coarse hair and bushy eyebrows

This severe form of MPS syndrome usually results in death in the second decade of life from heart failure and severe respiratory tract infections.

Konigsmark and Gorlin (1976) concluded that most Hurler syndrome patients have some degree of conductive hearing loss. In a temporal bone study of a child with MPS I-H, Keleman (1966) reported to have found extensive mesenchyme-like tissue within the epitympanum. Additionally, the mucous membrane of the middle ear covered and blocked the niches of both the oval and round windows. Incomplete development of middle ear structures was considered to have resulted from an arrest in temporal bone development during fetal life. Konigsmark and Gorlin (1976) also noted that the characteristically deformed nasopharynx associated with MPS I-H increases the susceptibility to upper respiratory infection, which in turn leads to a high incidence of recurrent otitis media.

Scheie Syndrome (MPS I-S)

The Scheie syndrome is milder than Hurler syndrome, with clinical detection difficult before age six. It was formerly known as MPS V, until biochemical studies revealed the same enzymatic involvement as in MPS I (alpha-L-iduronidase).

Biochemical complementation studies done by Galjaard (1980) support MPS I-H and I-S as being allelic mutations of the same gene. Typically, there is no associated mental retardation (Horowitz, 1979). The medical literature makes reference to cases of "mild" Hurler syndrome, which may in fact represent MPS I-S or MPS I-H/S compound heterozygotes. Konigsmark and Gorlin (1976) have estimated that not more than 10 to 20 percent of patients with MPS I-S have some form of hearing impairment. The degree of hearing loss is not severe and may result from combined dysfunction of conductive and sensorineural mechanisms.

Hunter Syndrome (MPS II)

Clinically, Hunter syndrome is similar to MPS I-H. It is distinguishable on the basis of a lack of corneal clouding, X-linked recessive inheritance, and greater clinical variability in terms of time of onset and severity. Mild forms of this disease may survive to adulthood and exhibit no mental deficits.

Of the MPS types, the otological and audiological characteristics associated with MPS II have been most extensively described. According to Leroy and Crocker (1966), some form of hearing impairment will accompany MPS II in approximately one-half of patients. The degree of hearing loss associated with MPS II is typically not severe and may be conductive, sensorineural, or mixed, although profound sensorineural hearing impairment has been reported in isolated cases (Young & Harper, 1982).

A detailed report of otological and audiological findings of two brothers with MPS II was presented by Peck (1984). These two siblings were followed for a two year period for otological management and behavioral and electrophysiological audiometric evaluations. Both had similar mixed hearing loss of a moderate degree bilaterally. The degree of hearing loss fluctuated for both depending upon the presence or absence of middle ear effusions. However, a large low frequency air bone gap persisted even after the insertion of ventilation tubes. The configuration of the bone conduction detection thresholds ranged from normal levels in the lower audiometric frequencies to approximately 60 dB at 4000 Hz. The combined low frequency conductive hearing loss and high frequency sensorineural hearing loss resulted in a flat bilateral hearing loss by air conduction of approximately 60 dB. Peck (1984) cautioned that, with children who have MPS II middle ear disorders can potentially mask coexisting sensorineural hearing loss, and therefore, follow-up after treatment of the middle ear disease is crucial to rule out the presence of a sensorineural component.

Sanfilippo Syndrome (MPS III)

Sanfilippo syndrome is associated with mild somatic changes and progressive dementia. Initial presentation may relate to behavioral disturbances. The clinical picture is also variable. Corneal clouding is not found in this condition. There appears to be a relatively low incidence (approximately 10 percent) of hearing impairment in patients with MPS III. As Konigsmark and Gorlin (1976) have pointed out, the characteristically aggressive nature of these patients has often made audiometric studies virtually impossible. In cases where hearing impairment has been documented, it appears late in childhood and tends to be progressive in nature (Konigsmark & Gorlin, 1976).

Morquio Syndrome (MPS IV)

The most striking clinical feature of Morquio syndrome is the severe bone dysplasia which results in dwarfism. Skeletal complications are more commonly seen in this syndrome than in other MPS syndromes. Deformity of the rib cage, kyphosis, and spinal cord compressions develop slowly with time. Although gross corneal clouding is not usually present, careful slit lamp examination may reveal fine corneal opacities. Mental development is unaffected and follows the distribution seen in the normal population.

In their audiometric study of 18 patients with MPS IV, Riedner and Levin (1977) found that 14 of 15 patients who were age 8 or older had either a mixed or sensorineural hearing impairment. In all but three of these patients, the degree of hearing loss was mild to moderate. Of the remaining three patients, two had moderate to severe mixed hearing losses bilaterally and one had a profound bilateral mixed loss of hearing. From the patient population studied, nearly 80 percent had a history of chronic or recurrent otitis media. On the basis of these findings, Riedner and Levin (1977) concluded that most patients with MPS IV can be expected to exhibit either a mixed or sensorineural hearing loss by the end of the first decade of life.

Maroteaux-Lamy Syndrome (MPS VI)

The clinical phenotype of Maroteaux-Lamy syndrome closely resembles that of MPS I-H, with the exception of normal intelligence in MPS VI. As in the other MPS syndromes, there exists much inter- and intrafamilial variability of affected individuals.

Hearing impairment is more often associated with the more severe form of MPS VI and is frequently conductive in nature, resulting from chronic otitis media (Konigsmark & Gorlin, 1976).

Speech

There is little information concerning speech and language changes in each of these MPS syndromes. Case study information (Sparks, 1984) has detailed the type and length of therapy for one form (Hunter) of MPS. Depending upon the degree of the signs available, the effects upon speech and language will be variable. When the form is severe, the patients may be expected to show deterioration of all forms of communication. In milder forms, the individuals may be capable of functioning adequately in academic and social situations with speech and language. The persistent upper respiratory function and chronic middle ear infections that may cause hearing impairment should be followed closely so as not to add further insult to the communication. Early diagnosis and routine evaluation of cognitive and linguistic function appear necessary to monitor changes in behavior.

Because the MPS conditions have both mild and severe forms, it should be noted that speech, language, and hearing difficulties also follow these wide ranges. In the mild cases, the individuals may show no major difficulties with communication whereas in the severe forms, the child may never develop normal speech and language skills. Further, several case studies (Sparks, 1984) have suggested that children so affected may lose early developmental milestones as the disease progresses. Cognitive function appears to follow the same pattern.

Management

Genetics and Medical

With the exception of MPS II (X-linked recessive) the MPS syndromes predominantly follow autosomal recessive inheritance. With the extreme clinical variability, careful delineation of the enzymatic defect is imperative in reaching the correct MPS biochemical diagnosis. Parents of a child with an autosomal recessive form will be at a 25 percent risk in subsequent pregnancies. Prenatal diagnosis via amniocentesis or chorionic villi sampling are options that should be discussed with the parents. Artifical insemination by donor may also be a viable alternative for some couples. In the case of X-linked inheritance, a carrier woman will have a 25 percent chance for an affected male child (i.e., 50 percent of male children will be at risk). Female children should be clinically normal, but are at a 50 percent risk to be a carrier and possibly have an affected son. Heterozygote detection is possible, which can confirm genotype and help refine the genetic counseling given.

Medical management has traditionally centered around symptomatic treatment. Corneal transplants have been performed in MPS I. It is still too early to assess the success of such experimental procedures as fibroblast (Dena, Muir, Benson, & Button, 1980) or bone marrow transplantation (Hobbs, Barret, & Chambers, 1981) in reversing or halting the progressive deterioration in individuals with severe varieties of MPS syndromes.

Hearing

Due to the range in both degree and type of hearing impairment which has been reported to occur in the mucopolysaccharidoses, as well as the range of other features, no singular approach to audiological management can be advised. Certainly, the incidence of hearing impairment in general and the possibility of progressive hearing impairment specifically warrants early audiometric assessment and a program of long-term audiological monitoring. In view of the possibility of additional visual, cognitive, and behavioral difficulties in particular, a team approach to management is viewed as essential with this group of syndromes.

Speech

Mild forms of the MPS syndromes may use traditional therapies to develop speech and language competency. In the severe forms, the parents, caregivers, and family unit should practice a variety of forms of communication (i.e., verbal and nonverbal) to enable the child to communicate as effectively as possible for as long as possible. Certainly, attention to auditory problems must be attended to routinely in order that hearing difficulties do not add to the cognitive or linguistic problems. Counseling with the family concerning language learning potential is strongly urged (Sparks, 1984).

Prognosis

The natural history will vary considerably according to the type of MPS problem and its severity. Individuals with mild forms of the disorder may function well in academic and social linguistic situations without need for traditional stimulation to achieve expected performance levels. Individuals with the severe forms of the disorder have a poor prognosis and deterioration of early skills is apparent in the later childhood years.

■ References

Dena, M. F., Muir, H., Benson, P., Button, L. (1980). Enzyme replacement therapy in the mucopolysaccharidoses by fibroblast transplantation. *Birth Defects: Original Article Series, 16*(1), 445–456.

Galjaard, H. (1980). *Genetic metabolic diseases* (1st ed., p. 114). Amsterdam: Elsevier North Holland.

Hobbs, J. R., Barret, A. J., & Chambers, D. (1981). Reversal of clinical features of Hurler's disease and biochemical improvement after treatment by bone-marrow transplantation. *Lancet, II,* 709–712.

Horowitz, A. L. (1979). The mucopolysaccharidoses: Clinical and biochemical correlations. *American Journal of Mental Deficiency, 84,* 113–123.

Keleman, G. (1966). Hurler's syndrome and the hearing organ. *Journal of Laryngology and Otology, 80,* 791–803.

Konigsmark, B. W., & Gorlin, R. J. (1976). *Genetic and metabolic deafness* (pp. 345–350). Philadelphia: W. B. Saunder.

Leroy, J. G., & Crocker, A. C. (1966). Clinical definition of Hunter–Hurler phenotypes: A review of 50 patients. *American Journal of Diseases of Children, 112,* 518–530.

Peck, J. E. (1984). Hearing loss in Hunter's syndrome: Mucopolysaccharidosis II. *Ear and Hearing, 5,* 243–246.

Riedner, E. D., & Levin, S. (1977). Hearing patterns in Morquio's syndrome (mucopolysaccharidosis IV). *Archives of Otolaryngology, 103,* 518–520.

Sparks, S. (1984). *Birth defects and speech and language disorders.* San Diego: College-Hill Press.

Spranger, J. (1983). The mucopolysaccharidoses. In A. E. H. Emery & D. L. Rimoin (Eds.), *Principles and practice of medical genetics* (Vol. 2, pp. 1339–1347). New York: Churchill Livingston.

Young, I. D., & Harper, P. S. (1982). Mild form of Hunter's syndrome: Clinical delineation based on 31 cases. *Archives of Diseases in Childhood, 57,* 828–836.

Oro-Facial-Digital Syndrome Type II
(OFD Type II; Mohr Syndrome)

■ Characteristics
Dysmorphology

A clinical diagnosis of oro-facial-digital syndrome (OFD) type II is made on the basis of characteristic oral, facial, and digital anomalies described by Mohr in 1941. OFD type II (Goodman & Gorlin, 1977) includes the features of (see list):

midline partial tongue clefts, lobate tongue, or tongue nodules

midline cleft lip

absent central incisors

broad or bifid nasal tip

lateral displacement of inner canthi

mandibular hypoplasia

polydactyly, partial reduplication of halluces

relative brachydactyly, syndactyly, or clinodactyly

conductive hearing deficit

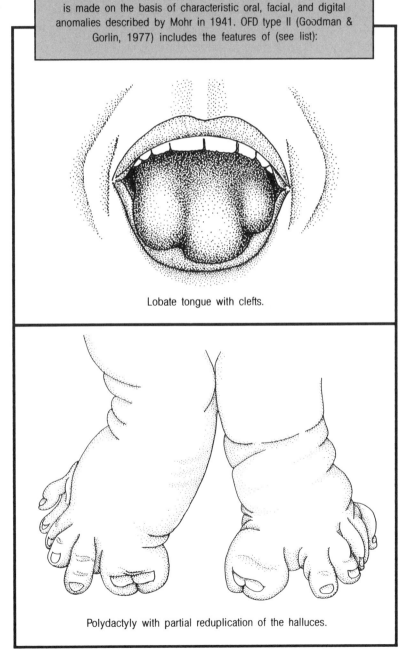

Lobate tongue with clefts.

Polydactyly with partial reduplication of the halluces.

This condition is significantly different from that of OFD type I. The latter has fibrous band clefting of the alveolar ridges, missing lateral incisors, sparse hair, and dry scalp. Clinical distinction is important as OFD type II is autosomal recessive (with the expectation of occurrence in both sexes) whereas OFD type I is not observed in male subjects, implying either X-linked dominant or sex limited dominant inheritance (Rimoin & Edgerton, 1967).

Hearing

External ear malformations observed in OFD type II include bilateral microtia and external auditory canal atresia. Middle ear anomalies have been described in some detail and include malformations of the stapes and incus, disarticulation of the incus and stapes, and stapes footplate fixation (Caldarelli, 1977).

Rimoin and Edgerton (1976) provided a detailed review of two siblings with OFD II. Although both reportedly had similar bilateral conductive hearing loss, middle ear exploration and surgical reconstruction had only been performed with the older sibling at the time of this report. Findings of the middle ear exploration included congenital malformation of the incus with total absence of the lenticular process and failure of the incus to articulate with the normal appearing stapes.

Hearing loss in patients with OFD II will be conductive in nature, resulting from atresic ear canals, congenital malformation of the ossicular chain, or chronic otitis media secondary to cleft palate. Differentiation of this conductive hearing loss resulting from chronic otitis media and that resulting from congenital ossicular chain abnormalities is of critical importance in the differential diagnostic process with OFD II patients.

Speech

The existence of a median cleft of the upper lip, if repaired, should not present any difficulties with respect to the production of speech. In cases where a cleft of the palate is present, typical cleft related problems may be expected. These include problems in childhood with sucking, swallowing, nasal regurgitation, nasal air emission, hypernasality, and the potential for abnormal compensatory articulations. Micrognathia may be severe enough to result in the production of oral distortions of sibilants, fricatives, and affricatives, related to abnormal tongue-mandible-maxilla relationships. Further distortion of orally articulated sounds may be expected to occur in the presence of a lobate tongue, depending on the degree of involvement, and in the absence of lower central incisors. The frequent occurrence of the conductive hearing loss may be expected to hamper the development of language. Finally, the presence of an intellectual handicap may be associated with developmental delay, poor gross motor control, learning disability, and school perform-ance problems.

There are no published data that refer specifically to the range of severity. Several authors have made reference to the point that these patients form a genetically heterogenous group, with vari-able expressivity (Fenton & Watt–Smith, 1985; Mattei & Ayme, 1983). There are some data to suggest that the degree of tongue in-volvement may be quite variable, ranging from one small lobule to a substantial number (Gencik & Gencikova, 1983).

Management

Genetics and Medical

Oro-facial-digital syndrome type II is autosomal recessive. Both parents of an affected child are presumed heterozygous carriers of the gene. Each subsequent pregnancy is at a 25 percent chance of a similarly affected individual, regardless of sex. However, an af-fected individual is unlikely to have affected children as long as marriage to a close relative (or similarly affected person) is avoided.

Hearing

Hearing aids, or surgery where indicated, can optimize hearing in individuals with oro-facial-digital syndrome type II.

Speech

Surgical treatment of clefts of the lip or palate may be performed to normalize the oral-nasal-pharyngeal area for aid in developing speech and swallowing activities. Treatment may, at some point in time, involve secondary surgery and prosthetic techniques. Surgery may also be considered in cases where hypoplasia of the mandible is severe in order to bring the mandible back into a more normal relationship with the maxilla. Lobulation of the tongue may be treated surgically as well, particularly in situations where the condi-tion interferes with respiration, swallowing, or speech intelligibility.

Speech and language therapy will most likely be a part of the treatment of these patients. The development of articulation and language may be expected to be compromised by the presence of a conductive hearing loss or intellectual involvement. In the case of intellectual involvement, special education personnel may also be needed.

Prognosis

Intelligence and life span are thought to be equivalent to the nonaf-fected population distribution. Prognosis will depend on the degree of expressivity of the syndrome. Obviously, the timely and successful surgical treatment of the malformed incus, cleft lip or palate, and lobate tongue will improve the chances for normal speech and language development. Early intervention and close follow-up will optimize the development of speech and language by these individuals.

■ References

Caldarelli, D. (1977). Congenital middle ear anomalies associated with craniofacial and skeletal syndromes. In B. Jaffe (Ed.), *Hearing loss in children* (pp. 310–340). Baltimore: University Park Press.

Fenton, O., & Watt–Smith, S. (1985). The spectrum of the oro-facial-digital syndromes. *British Journal of Plastic Surgery, 38,* 532–539.

Gencik, A., & Gencikova, A. (1983). Mohr syndrome in two siblings. *Journal de Genetique Humaine, 31,* 307–315.

Goodman, R., & Gorlin, R. (1977). *Atlas of the face in genetic disorders.* St. Louis: C. V. Mosby.

Mattei, J., & Ayme, S. (1983). Syndrome of polydactyly, cleft lip. lingual hamartomas, renal hypoplasia, hearing loss, and psychomotor retardation: Variant of the Mohr syndrome or a new syndrome? *Journal of Medical Genetics, 20,* 433–435.

Mohr, O. L. (1941). A hereditary lethal syndrome in man. *Avhandlinger Utgitt av Norsk Videnskaps Akademi I Oslo, 14,* 1–18.

Rimoin, D., & Edgerton, M. (1967). Genetic and clinical heterogeneity in the oral-facial-digital syndromes. *Journal of Pediatrics, 71,* 94–102.

Pendred Syndrome
(Deafness and Goiter)

■ Characteristics
Dysmorphology

congenital sensorineural hearing impairment

defective thyroid hormonogenesis

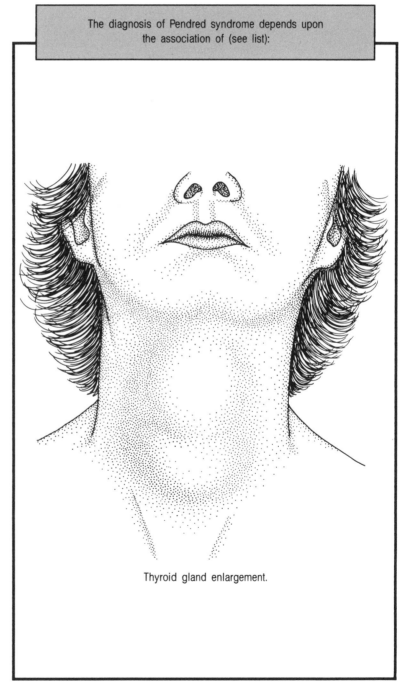

The diagnosis of Pendred syndrome depends upon the association of (see list):

Thyroid gland enlargement.

The thyroid gland may be moderately enlarged. Functionally, there is a mild problem with thyroid hormone production, but most individuals have normal thyroid hormone levels. Forty percent show some evidence of hypothyroidism in their earlier years. Many of the younger subjects seen with the syndrome show skeletal delays in maturation, even with medication given to correct the thyroid problem. Some subjects also show mental retardation as a part of the syndrome.

Hearing

The incidence of the syndrome has been estimated from between 1 in 100,000 (Nilsson, Borgsfors, Gamstorp, Holst, & Liden, 1964) to 8 in 100,000 (Fraser, 1965). Furthermore, it has been estimated that between 4 to 10 percent of those with congenital sensorineural hearing impairment have Pendred syndrome (Illum, Kiaer, Hvidberg-Hansen, & Sondergaard, 1972). Thould and Scowen (1964) found that of 822 children with sensorineural hearing impairment of unknown etiology, 15, or approximately two percent, had the syndrome. No significant difference in the number of male or female subjects affected was found in this sample.

Tomographic studies performed by Illum and colleagues (1972) revealed the presence of a Mondini defect in 7 and possibly 8 of the 15 cases studied. A histological description of the temporal bones of a case with Pendred syndrome was reported by Hvidberg-Hansen and Jorgensen (1968). The bony inner ears were bilaterally symmetrical and of Mondini type, with the basal cochlear turn present and apical turns forming a large common cavity (see Figures 3-10 & 3-11). Although some supporting cells were noted along the organ of Corti, no hair cells were evident. Furthermore, the tectorial membranes were completely absent.

Despite laboratory attempts (Ritter, 1967), a cause and effect relationship between the thyroid disorder and hearing impairment has not been demonstrated. Batsakis and Nishiyama (1962) concluded that the auditory disorder is not due to the thyroid problem.

The degree of sensorineural hearing loss can vary from mild to profound and is, in most cases, bilaterally symmetrical. Konigsmark and Gorlin (1976) have estimated that hearing loss will be severe to profound in more than 50 percent of individuals with this syndrome. In the previously referenced report of 15 cases with Pendred syndrome by Illum and colleagues (1972), 12 had pure tone average hearing levels greater than 90 dB HTL, with 4 of the 12 having no measurable hearing sensitivity. A consistent finding for audiometric configuration in cases with Pendred syndrome is the greater loss of hearing for frequencies above approximately 500 Hz (see Figure 3-12a, b). A progressive decrease in hearing sensitivity has been observed to occur during childhood (Illum et al., 1972).

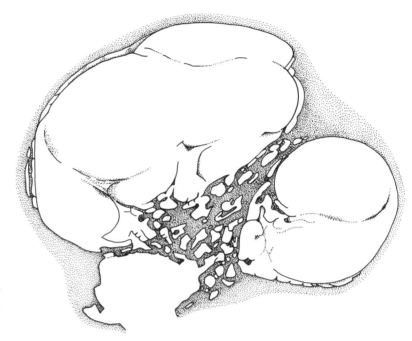

FIGURE 3–10:
Left temporal bone in Mondini cochlea.

Additionally, isolated cases have been reported in which hearing sensitivity is near normal in one ear (Fraser, 1965).

In addition to Pendred syndrome, hearing loss is associated with two other thyroid disorders, including adult myxedema and endemic cretinism. The hearing loss associated with adult myxedema may be either conductive, sensorineural, or mixed in nature.

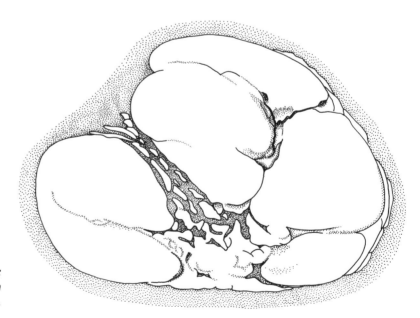

FIGURE 3–11:
Right temporal bone in Mondini cochlea.

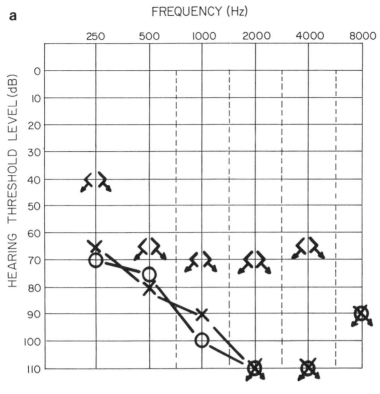

a

FREQUENCY (Hz)

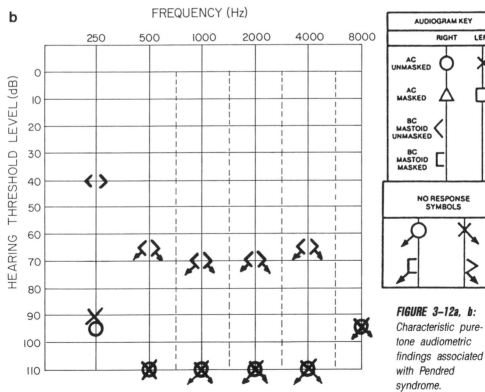

b

FREQUENCY (Hz)

AUDIOGRAM KEY

	RIGHT	LEFT
AC UNMASKED	◯	✕
AC MASKED	△	☐
BC MASTOID UNMASKED	ᐸ	ᐳ
BC MASTOID MASKED	[	]

NO RESPONSE SYMBOLS

FIGURE 3-12a, b: Characteristic pure-tone audiometric findings associated with Pendred syndrome.

165

The hearing loss will be conductive if edema of the middle ear or Eustachian tube is present or sensorineural when myxedematous infiltration affects endolymphatic circulation (Batsakis & Nishiyama, 1962). In endemic cretinism, as in Pendred syndrome, all cases exhibit some degree of sensorineural hearing loss, typically within the range of severe to profound.

Speech

With hearing impairment present early in life, many of the children have severe speech and language learning problems that result in placement in special classes or schools for hearing impaired children. Early reports from the literature classified many of the persons affected with this disease as being "mute." Difficulties in vowel differentiation, consonant sound development, and sound-symbol association may be expected. Language skills, including vocabulary development, syntactic growth, and pragmatic aspects of language learning, will be absent or severely delayed unless direct management is provided.

Management

Genetics and Medical

An autosomal recessive pattern of inheritance have been demonstrated (Fraser, 1965; Thould & Scowen, 1964). This implies a 25 percent recurrence risk for parents to have another affected child. As expected with autosomal recessive inheritance, both sexes are equally affected. In cases where thyroid function is borderline normal or low, administration of an exogenous thyroid preparation may help minimize symptomatology.

Hearing

Severe hearing impairment, if diagnosed early, may be managed with effective auditory training, speech reading, and amplification and speech rehabilitation as with any child who is hearing impaired. In view of the possibility of progressive hearing loss, routine audiological monitoring is strongly encouraged.

Speech

Speech production and language development will depend upon the medical treatment of the disease, degree of hearing loss, monitoring effective use of residual hearing and the cognitive abilities of the child. Traditional management programs for children who are hearing impaired should be considered. Parent training, preschool education programs, personal amplification, as well as individual speech and language therapy should be considered as important factors in any management program.

Prognosis

The prognosis for each individual depends upon the severity of the disease, the degree of hearing loss, and other possible factors that could hinder communication development. In general, the prognosis should be no worse than that of other children or adults who are severely hearing impaired. Early diagnosis and medical and behavioral treatment will improve the prognosis for later speech and language skill development or maintenance.

■ References

Batsakis, J., & Nishiyama, R. (1962). Deafness with sporadic goitre. *Archives of Otolaryngology, 76,* 401–406.

Fraser, G. R. (1965). Association of congenital deafness with goitre (Pendred's syndrome): A study of 207 families. *Annuals of Human Genetics London, 28,* 201–249.

Hvidberg–Hansen, J., & Jorgensen, M. (1968). The inner ear in Pendred's syndrome. *Acta Otolaryngologica, 66,* 129–135.

Illum, P., Kiaer, H. W., Hvidberg–Hansen, J., & Sondergaard, G. (1972). Fifteen cases of Pendred's syndrome. *Archives of Otolaryngology, 96,* 297–304.

Konigsmark, B., & Gorlin, R. (1976). *Genetic and metabolic deafness* (pp. 330–335). Toronto: W. B. Saunders.

Nilsson, L. Borgfors, N., Gamstorp. I., Holst, H. E., & Liden, G. (1964). Nonendemic goiter and deafness. *Acta Paediatricia, 3,* 117–131.

Ritter, F. (1967). The effects of hypothyroidism upon the ear, nose and throat. *Laryngoscope, 77,* 1427–1479.

Thould, A. K., & Scowen, E. F. (1964). The syndrome of congenital deafness and simple goitre. *Journal of Endocrinology, 30,* 69–77.

Refsum Syndrome
(Phytanic Acid Storage Disease)

■ Characteristics
Dysmorphology

retinitis pigmentosa

chronic polyneuritis

cerebellar ataxia

progressive sensorineural hearing impairment

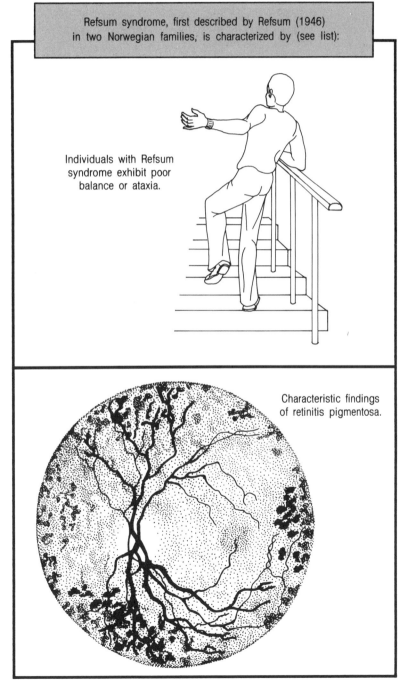

Refsum syndrome, first described by Refsum (1946) in two Norwegian families, is characterized by (see list):

Individuals with Refsum syndrome exhibit poor balance or ataxia.

Characteristic findings of retinitis pigmentosa.

There are other neurological conditions with overlapping signs and symptoms, but Refsum syndrome is reserved for cases in which a biochemical abnormality of phytanic acid storage is demonstrated. Elevations of phytanic acid may be demonstrated in either plasma or tissues. The retinal degeneration often manifests as night blindness and loss of visual fields. Cataracts and nystagmus are also observed (Fryer, Winckleman, Ways, & Swanson, 1971). In the nervous system, ataxia and weakness are generally found in childhood, with the legs deteriorating first, then the arms. In addition, anosmia, paresthesia, pain, and a lack of superficial reflexes are noted. In about half of the patients reviewed, heart disease was present. Approximately 75 percent show skeletal deformities including spondylitis, exostoses of the sternum, kyphoscoliosis, and, occasionally, "claw" hand.

Hearing

Approximately one-half of patients with Refsum syndrome demonstrate progressive sensorineural hearing impairment (Konigsmark, 1969). When hearing impairment is present, it most often begins in the second or third decade of life and progresses slowly over time. Hallpike (1967) described a variety of temporal bone anomalies for a patient with severe sensorineural hearing loss secondary to Refsum syndrome. His findings include a degeneration of the stria vascularis, collapse of Reissner's membrane, loss of spiral ganglion cells, and atrophy of the organ of Corti.

Bergsmark and Djupesland (1968) described the sensorineural hearing loss associated with Refsum syndrome as possibly more severe on one side and typically more predominant in the higher audiometric frequency region, at least during the earlier stages of progression.

Fleming (1957) provided a complete review of a brother and sister with this syndrome. According to his report, the brother began to experience a loss of hearing at age 25 and was described to be "totally deaf" in both ears by age 30. His sister who was age 26 at the time of this case study, reported a fairly rapid deterioration in hearing ability in both ears during her teen years. She reportedly retained sufficient residual hearing to "get along quite well" with a hearing aid. These two siblings, whose parents were first cousins, developed other progressive changes associated with Refsum syndrome.

Speech

Speech difficulties accompanying the syndrome should mirror the typical characteristics of persons with a progressive (acquired) sensorineural hearing loss. This usually involves loss of precision of sibilants, particularly in the final position of words, loss of precision of vowels, increases in vocal intensity and vocal frequency, and alteration of speech rate. In the later stages, alternations in resonance balance (hypernasality) may also occur. The ataxic condition, if it progresses from the periphery to the speech musculature, may include characteristics of articulation imprecision, vocal quality problems including harsh voice and increased variability in loudness and pitch, and alterations in stress rate of speaking. Little information, however, is available concerning the trends of these characteristics as the patient's condition progresses.

Management

Genetics and Medical

Of the 50 published cases with the syndrome, all pedigrees were compatible with autosomal recessive transmission. Parental consanguinity was apparent in half of those cases.

Parents of an affected individual are at a 25 percent recurrence risk. Because the syndrome is sometimes diagnosed at a later age, most family planning may have already occurred. Medically, attention is directed to limiting accumlation of phytanic acid by dietary manipulation. Foods rich in phytanic acid precursors are avoided (dairy products, beef, and mutton), but its wide distribution in foodstuffs makes this strategy difficult to follow (Steinberg, 1978). Some clinical improvement or stabilization has been observed but long-term follow-up will be necessary. A combination of diet and plasmapheresis has also been claimed to demonstrate benefits (Gibbard, Page, Billimoria, & Retsas, 1979; Moser et al., 1980). Management should also include careful cardiac assessment to help reduce associated morbidity.

Hearing

As for other syndromes that have associated sensorineural hearing impairment, frequent and careful monitoring of hearing sensitivity is strongly advised. It should be recalled that when hearing impairment occurs, it most often begins within the second or third decade of life. In the event of sensorineural hearing impairment, a comprehensive rehabilitation program should be designed and implemented (see management considerations for Usher syndrome).

Speech

Dysarthrias associated with the ataxic condition may be treated using methods of articulatory, phonatory, and rate control as noted by Rosenbek and LaPointe (1985). In the later stages of the disease process, augmentative communication devices should be used to aid in communication with family and caregivers.

Prognosis

The course of the disease is variable. Typically, the progression is slow with general deterioration leading to total incapacitation in the third or fourth decade. Because the disease is progressive, management procedures are designed to provide quality of life for as long as possible.

■ References

Bergsmark, J., & Djupesland, G. (1968). Heredopathia atactica polyneuritiformis (Refsum's disease). An audiological examination of two patients. *European Neurology, 1,* 122–130.

Fleming, R. (1957). Refsum's syndrome. *Neurology, 7,* 476–479.

Fryer, D. G., Winckleman, A. C., Ways, P. O., & Swanson, A. C. (1971). Refsum's disease. *Neurology, 21,* 162–167.

Gibbard, F. B., Page, N. G. R., Billimoria, J. D., & Retsas, S. (1979). Heredopathia atactia polyneuritiformis (Refsum's disease) treated by diet and plasma-exchange. *Lancet, 1,* 575–578.

Hallpike, C. S. (1967). Observations on the structural basis of two rare varieties of hereditary deafness. In A. V. de Reuch & J. Knight (Eds.), *Myotatic, kinesthetic and vestibular mechanisms* (pp. 285–294). Boston: Little, Brown & Co.

Konigsmark, B. W. (1969). Hereditary deafness in man: II. *New England Journal of Medicine, 281,* 774–778.

Moser, H. W., Braine, H., Pyeritz, R. E., Ullman, D. D., Murray, C., & Asbury, A. K. (1980). Therapeutic trial of plasmapheresis in Refsum disease and in Fabry disease. *Birth Defects Original Article Series, 16*(1), 491–497.

Refsum, S. (1946). Heredopathia atactica polyneruitiformis; familial syndrome not hitherto described; contribution to clinical study of hereditary disease of nervous system. *Acta Psychiatrica Scandinavia, Supplement 38*(1).

Rosenbek, J. C., & LaPointe, L. (1985). The dysarthrias: Description, diagnosis and treatment. In D. F. Johns (Ed.), *Clinical management of neurogenic communicative disorders* (2nd ed.). Boston: Little, Brown & Co.

Steinberg, D. (1978). Phytanic acid storage disease: (Refsum's syndrome). In J. B. Stanbury, J. B. Wyngaarden, & D. S. Fredrickson (Eds.), *The metabolic basis of inherited disease* (4th ed., pp. 688–706). New York: McGraw-Hill.

Riley-Day Syndrome
(Familial Dysautonomia)

■ Characteristics
Dysmorphology

First described in detail by Riley, Day, Greely, and Langford (1949), Riley–Day syndrome involves a primary disturbance of the autonomic nervous system with a variable amount of central nervous system involvement (Halpern, Hochberg, & Rees, 1967). Features include (see list):

swallowing difficulties in infancy

lack of tearing

absence of fungiform papillae of the tongue

dysarthria or dysphagia

increased sweating

indifference to pain

labile blood pressure

emotional lability

blotching of the skin

poor coordination

Insensitivity to pain and a predisposition toward blotchiness of the skin (cutis marmorata) are features exhibited by individuals with Riley-Day syndrome.

The syndrome is usually diagnosed between the ages of 2 and 10 (Francois, 1977), although features such as the swallowing difficulty and indifference to pain may be noted earlier. Motor coordination, in particular that of fine and repetitive movements, is impaired in these patients (Brunt & McKusick, 1970; Halpern et al., 1967). Francois (1977) referred to a psychomotor retardation involving delayed motor development milestones, and also suggested that mental retardation may be observed. However, Brunt and McKusick (1970) stated that there does not appear to be any intellectual impairment associated with this syndrome. A detailed investigation of intellectual development in this population was conducted by Welton, Clayson, Axelrod, and Levine (1979). Their results indicated that the proportion of familial dysautonomia patients scoring within the average range of intelligence was similar to that found in the general population. Further, they determined that the intellectual function curve for this population was negatively skewed. This was attributed to uneven anxiety control, and deficits resulting from experiential limitations.

Hearing

The existence of a moderate to severe hearing loss was reported by Francois (1977). However, Halpern and colleagues (1967) concluded that the incidence of hearing impairment in children with familial dysautonomia did not differ substantially from that found in the general population. This has also been the observation of others (Siegel–Sadewitz & Shprintzen, 1982).

Speech

The most significant aspect of this syndrome related to speech and language is the pronounced dysfunction in gross and fine motor control. The speech and language characteristics of this population have been investigated by de Hirsch and Jansky (1956) and Halpern and colleagues (1967). Speech production is typically dysarthric in nature. Sound distortions occur with much greater frequency than either substitutions or omissions. Of the 15 percent of sounds misarticulated by the group in the study by Halpern and colleagues, 83 percent were distortions, 12.5 percent were substitutions, and 4.5 percent were omissions. This pattern is consistent with dysarthria. All but one subject exhibited noticeable hypernasality, and 4 of 11 drooled considerably.

Similarly, de Hirsch and Jansky (1956) found that the majority of their tests of movement and control of peripheral speech organs (e.g., lip and tongue movement, diadochokinesis) showed deviations. Further, 10 of their 12 children had poor voice quality, with 9 having excessive nasality. A number of children demonstrated variations in loudness. De Hirsch and Jansky (1956) related these speech patterns to those typically seen in patients with bulbar dysfunction.

As stated earlier, intellectual function does not appear to be grossly deviant. Welton and colleagues (1979) addressed the deleterious effects of motor incoordination on intellectual potential in these patients. However, 67 percent of their study group were attending or had graduated from mainstream classes in regular schools, whereas only 29 percent attended special schools. This is in contrast to data from Sak, Smith, and Dancis (1967) that indicated that the majority are placed either in special classes or special schools. As suggested by Welton and colleagues (1979), this observation may reflect the medical, educational, and vocational management of this population.

There are few data regarding range in severity of the speech problems. Speech patterns do not appear to vary considerably across subjects, although the data base is small.

Management

Genetics and Medical

Virtually all patients are of Ashkenazi Jewish ancestry (Gorlin, Pindborg, & Cohen, 1976). Incidence in that population is 1 in 10,000 to 20,000 (McKusick, Norum, Farkas, Brunt, & Mahloudji, 1967), with roughly equal sex distribution. As with other autosomal recessive conditions, parents of an affected child have a 25 percent recurrence risk in any subsequent pregnancy. As yet, there is no reliable prenatal diagnostic technique available. Artifical insemination by donor may be an option for some couples.

Medical treatment is often directed at preventing problems from developing or worsening. The lack of tearing predisposes to corneal ulcerations and routine application of artifical tears is recommended. Anticipatory guidance of parents and teachers can also minimize trauma or inquiry due to the individual's insensitivity to pain. The relative lack of sensation also predisposes to orthopedic concerns, such as scoliosis. The increased incidence of respiratory infection due to aspiration and swallowing difficulties needs to be aggressively treated in infancy. General anesthesia risks are also higher for this patient. Mortality is high. Thirty-six percent of the 210 patients studied by Brunt and McKusick (1970) had died by the time of data collection. The most frequent cause of death was recurrent respiratory infection. According to Francois (1977), mortality is high before the age of 20.

Speech

Early behavioral management is essential in the treatment of this population. It is important to provide a variety of experiences and opportunities to develop intellectual function in an attempt to counteract the reported deleterious effects of motor dysfunction. With respect to speech or articulation proficiency, there are no published reports of treatment or its effect. Given that the patterns of speech demonstrated by familial dysautonomia patients resemble those of dysarthric patients, speech therapies described for that population may be attempted. Wertz (1978) and Helmick (1980) discussed typical approaches to the treatment of flaccid dysarthrias. Techniques recommended to improve performance include attention to posture of the upper torso and articulatory system, muscle strength, rate reduction, overarticulation and maintenance of appropriate levels of voice frequency and intensity, and vocal variability.

Although placement in a regular school appears now to be more the norm, school performance should be closely monitored in order to provide appropriate academic assistance if needed.

Prognosis

Survival data based on older studies are not good. As already stated, death often occurs before the age of 20. Better attention to the previously mentioned medical concerns should help to decrease the morbidity and mortality associated with this syndrome. In terms of speech performance, the disorder is not reported to be progressive. If the patient population reported by Halpern and colleagues (1967) is typical, the speech of these children is not severely disordered (at least in an articulation test context). Early and appropriate intervention should then be expected to result in intelligible, functional speech.

■ References

Brunt, P., & McKusick, V. (1970). Familial dysautonomia: A report of genetic and clinical studies, with a review of the literature. *Medicine, 49,* 343–374.

de Hirsch, K., & Jansky, J. (1956). Language investigation of children suffering from familial dysautonomia. *Journal of Speech and Hearing Disorders, 21,* 450–460.

Francois, J. (1977). The Riley–Day syndrome: Familial dysautonomy, central autonomic dysfunction. *Ophthalmologica (Basel), 174,* 20–34.

Gorlin, R., Pindborg, J., & Cohen, M. (1976). *Syndromes of the head and neck.* New York: McGraw-Hill.

Halpern, H., Hochberg, I., & Rees, N. (1967). Speech and hearing characteristics in familial dysautonomia. *Journal of Speech and Hearing Research, 10,* 361–366.

Helmick, J. (1980). Speech characteristics of two children with Moebius syndrome. *Journal of Childhood Communicative Disorders, 4,* 19–28.

McKusick, V., Norum, R., Farkas, H., Brunt, J., & Mahloudji, M. (1967). The Riley–Day syndrome: Observation on genetics and survivorship. *Israel Journal of Medical Science, 3,* 372–379.

Riley, C., Day, R., Greely, D., & Langford, W. (1949). Central autonomic dysfunction with defective lacrimation (report of 5 cases). *Pediatrics, 3,* 468–478.

Sak, J., Smith, A., & Dancis, J. (1967). Psychometric evaluations of children with familial dysautonomia. *American Journal of Psychiatry, 124,* 5–12.

Siegel–Sadewitz, V., & Shprintzen, R. J. (1982). The relationship of communication disorders to syndrome identification. *Journal of Speech and Hearing Disorders, 47,* 338–354.

Welton, W., Clayson, D., Axelrod, F., & Levine, D. (1979). Intellectual development and familial dysautonomia. *Pediatrics, 63,* 708–712.

Wertz, R. (1978). Neuropathologies of speech and language: An introduction to patient management. In D. F. Johns (Ed.), *Clinical management of neurogenic communicative disorders* (1st ed.). Boston: Little, Brown & Co.

Usher Syndrome
(Retinitis Pigmentosa and Congenital Deafness)

■ Characteristics
Dysmorphology

retinitis pigmentosa (RP) similar to the autosomal recessive form of isolated RP in which onset is in the first or second decade of life

congenital hearing loss ranging from moderate to severe, but not usually of a progressive nature

The hereditary aspect of the congenital hearing loss associated with Usher syndrome was described by Usher (1935). Since then, the variability in clinical phenotype has become better delineated as (see list):

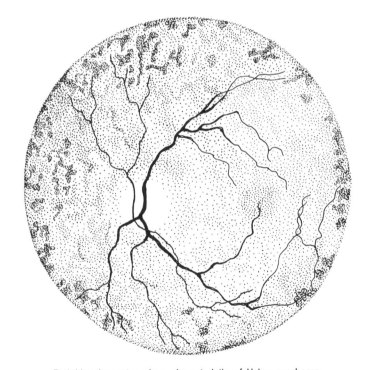

Retinitis pigmentosa is a characteristic of Usher syndrome.

In childhood, this syndrome is characterized by poor adaptation to darkness (night blindness), with progression to limited peripheral vision that becomes increasingly apparent during the teenage years. In later adulthood there is degeneration of central vision.

Hearing

Sensorineural hearing loss is one of the cardinal features of Usher syndrome (Konigsmark & Gorlin, 1976). It is estimated that 3 per 100,000 persons from the general population have Usher syndrome. Moreover, 3 to 10 percent of all children with a severe profound hearing loss and 50 percent of all deaf and blind adults may have Usher syndrome (Fraser, 1964; Vernon, 1969).

Histopathologically, the hearing impairment is due to the incomplete development or marked atrophy observed at the basal end of the organ of Corti in the cochlea. There is also severe atrophy of the stria vascularis and the spiral ganglion (Buch & Jorgensen, 1963).

The hearing loss associated with Usher syndrome is usually more pronounced at high than at low frequencies (see Figure 3–13). In most cases, the results obtained from behavioral and audiological tests (e.g., SISI, Bekesy, Speech Recognition test) are consistent

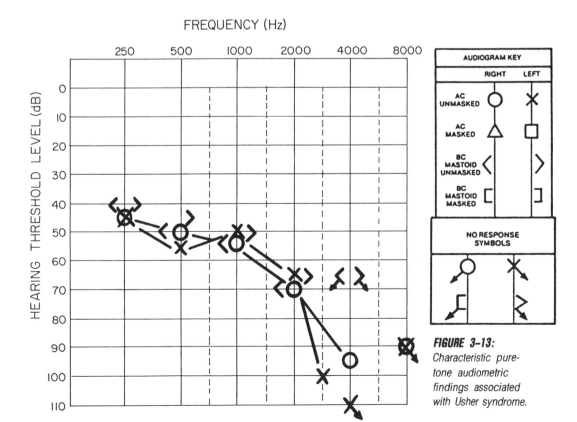

FIGURE 3–13: *Characteristic pure-tone audiometric findings associated with Usher syndrome.*

with a hearing loss of cochlear origin (Hallgren, 1959; Kloepfer, Languaite, & McLaurin, 1966; McLeod, McConnell, Sweeney, Cooper, & Nance, 1971). In some rare cases, central hearing impairments have been observed (McLeod et al., 1971).

A large proportion of persons with Usher syndrome (as many as 90 percent) display some form of vestibular problems. The severity and the specific type of vestibular disorder are quite variable (McLeod et al., 1971).

Of the 177 cases investigated by Hallgren (1959), 90 percent exhibited a severe or profound bilateral sensorineural hearing loss. The remaining cases displayed a sensorineural hearing loss ranging from mild to moderately severe (i.e., average hearing loss in the speech frequencies ranging from 30 to 70 dB HL). Other investigations have substantiated these findings (Kloepfer et al., 1966; McLeod et al., 1971). However, based on anecdotal evidence, Vernon (1974) suggested that a significantly larger number of individuals with the syndrome may have a moderate hearing loss.

Speech

The communication disorders associated with Usher syndrome may be seen primarily as the result of the hearing impairment. As in cases of comparable hearing impairment from other causes, there is a trend toward poor articulation of the high frequency sound elements (i.e., /s/, /f/, /sh/), changes in voiced and voiceless distinctions and speech rate, and overall deterioration in the intelligibility of speech. An increase in hypernasality and slight nasal air emission may occur as the speech production skills decrease in accuracy. If reduced cognitive function also occurs, it serves to delay vocabulary and syntactic development as well as the subtle skills of pragmatics of the communicative situation. The general language deficits may also have a central origin which may be mental age inconsistent (Vernon, 1969).

Management

Genetics and Medical

The variability in Usher syndrome can be quite extensive (McLeod et al., 1971). Usher syndrome overlaps other syndromes that are associated with retinitis pigmentosa and congenital hearing loss. These syndromes include Refsum syndrome, Laurence-Moon-Biedl syndrome, Alstrom syndrome, Cockayne syndrome, Kearn syndrome, and Hallgren syndrome (Vernon, 1974).

Effective management of an individual with Usher syndrome should begin with early diagnostic procedures such as: electroretinography, electroculography, dark adaptation recording, visual field testing, ophthalmological examination, and detailed electrophysiological and behavioral measures of hearing sensitivity. This early diagnosis will then lead to more effective rehabilitation through genetic and psychological counseling, and speech, language, and hearing habilitation.

Genetic counseling should be made available to individuals who have or are carriers of the syndrome (Harrod, 1978; Hicks, 1978; Vernon, 1974). Although the possibility of rare X-linked cases exist, the overwhelming majority of cases follow autosomal recessive inheritance. Parents of an affected child have a 25 percent risk for recurrence in any subsequent pregnancy. It is interesting to note that minor audiologic abnormalities have been reported among obligate carriers of Usher syndrome (Kloepfer et al., 1966; McLeod et al., 1971).

It is very important to provide individuals with all the information necessary to help them understand the disabilities associated with the syndrome. Individuals with Usher syndrome should also be provided with psychological counseling to help them cope with (and emotionally accept) the handicaps and the progressive nature of the syndrome (Hicks & Hicks, 1981).

Hearing

All individuals in programs for children who are hearing impaired should undergo a thorough screening program to identify Usher syndrome. Relatives of identified cases of Usher syndrome should also undergo audiological and ophthalmologic screening tests (Vernon, 1974).

Individuals with Usher syndrome should be fitted with an appropriate prosthetic device. In most cases, hearing aids should be recommended. When there is no residual hearing, other prosthetic devices such as a vibrotactile aid or a cochlear implant may be of benefit. The method of communication of choice will vary depending on the severity of the hearing and visual impairment (Kramer, Sullivan, & Hirsch, 1979).

Depending on age and specific degree of visual and hearing impairment, appropriate and individualized rehabilitation programs should be designed for individuals with Usher syndrome. The rehabilitation program may include regular evaluation, vision health care, orientation and mobility training, learning new adapted methods of communication, learning braille, or vocational training.

Speech

Because of the variability in the expressivity of the disorder in younger years, and with the progression toward deaf and blind conditions in later years, management of communication skills must be related to the number and severity of disabilities affecting reception of speech and language and the production of linguistically derived speech elements. Depending upon the nature of the hearing impairment and the cognitive abilities of the individual, language stimulation programs should begin as soon as the disease is detected. Speech habilitation should follow fitting of appropriate amplification systems using traditional aural teaching techniques. These techniques should allow the individual to monitor his or her articulation skills to produce the most effective quality possible.

Prognosis

The hearing loss is most often severe or profound and it is not reversible. Because the accompanying visual impairment is permanent and progressive, the prognosis for Usher syndrome is not good. In the early years, many of the individuals affected with the disorder function as speakers who are hearing impaired. With the progression of the visual defects, they are thrust into an ever more isolated environment. Because there is, at present, no known treatment for retinitis pigmentosa, and because the sensorineural hearing loss may become profound, counseling should begin early and continue as the condition worsens. Many individuals with Usher syndrome are forced to retire from the work force at a fairly young age (Konigsmark & Gorlin, 1976). Traditional auditory and speech management programs usually provide the only outlet for palliative care.

■ References

Buch, N. H., & Jorgensen, M. B. (1963). Pathological studies in deafness. *Archives of Otolaryngology, 77,* 247–253.

Fraser, G. R. (1964). Profound childhood deafness. *Journal of Medical Genetics, 1,* 118–151.

Hallgren, V. (1959). Retinitis pigmentosa combined with congenital deafness; with vestibulo-cerebellar ataxia and mental abnormality in a proportion of cases. A clinical geneticostatistical study. *Acta Psychiatrica Scandinavia,* (Suppl. 138), 1–101.

Harrod, M. J. E. (1978). Genetic counseling for Usher syndrome patients and their families. *American Annals of the Deaf, 123,* 380–388.

Hicks, W. (1978). Continuing education for deaf-blind youth and adults. *American Annals for the Deaf, 123,* 399–405.

Hicks, W., & Hicks, D. E. (1981). The Ushers syndrome adolescent: Programming implications for school administrators, teachers and residential advisors. *American Annals of the Deaf, 126,* 422–431.

Kloepfer, H. W., Languaite, J. K., & McLaurin, J. W. (1966). The hereditary syndrome of deafness in retinitis pigmentosa. *Laryngoscope, 76,* 850–862.

Konigsmark, B. W., & Gorlin, R. J. (1976). *Genetic and metabolic deafness.* Toronto: W. B. Saunders.

Kramer, L. C., Sullivan, R. F., & Hirsch, L. M. (1979). *Audiological evaluation and aural rehabilitation of the deaf-blind adult.* Sands Point, NY: Helen Keller National Center for the Deaf-Blind Youths and Adults.

McLeod, A. C., McConnell, F., Sweeney, A., Cooper, M., & Nance, W. (1971). Clinical variation in Usher syndrome. *Archives of Otolaryngology, 94,* 321–334.

Usher, C. H. (1935). Bowman's lecture on a few hereditary eye affections. *Transactions of the Ophthalmological Society of the United Kingdom, 55,* 164.

Vernon, M. (1969). Usher syndrome — deafness and progressive blindness. Clinical cases, prevention, theory and literature survey. *Journal of Chronic Diseases, 22,* 133–151.

Vernon, M. (1974). Overview of Usher syndrome: Congenital deafness and progressive loss of vision. *American Annals of the Deaf, 76,* 101–105.

Walters, J. W. (1978). Effective visual screening of the hearing impaired. *American Annals of the Deaf, 123,* 405–416.

Oto-Palatal-Digital Syndrome
(OPD Syndrome: Taybi Syndrome)

■ Characteristics
Dysmorphology

hearing impairment

cleft palate

generalized bone dysplasia manifesting as short and broad distal phalanges and limitation of elbow extension

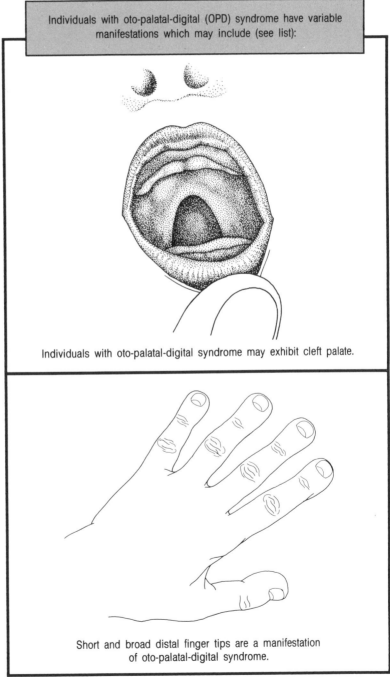

Individuals with oto-palatal-digital (OPD) syndrome have variable manifestations which may include (see list):

Individuals with oto-palatal-digital syndrome may exhibit cleft palate.

Short and broad distal finger tips are a manifestation of oto-palatal-digital syndrome.

The facies may also exhibit an antimongoloid slant of the palpebral fissures and a broad nasal bridge. Dudding, Gorlin, and Langer (1967) reported on the consistent finding of mild mental retardation, with IQs between 75 and 90. These reports were supported by Goodman and Gorlin (1977), but the relative contribution of hearing loss to a perceived intellectual deficit remains uncertain.

Hearing

The presence of bilateral conductive hearing impairment has been described in the majority of reported cases of OPD syndrome (Buran & Duvall, 1967; Dudding et al., 1967; Podoshin, Heymans, & Fradis, 1976). The conductive impairment results from either congenital abnormalities of the ossicular chain, otitis media secondary to cleft palate, or both in combination.

Otological findings for three male siblings with OPD syndrome were reported by Buran and Duvall (1967). Unilateral tympanotomy was performed with two siblings. Very thickened ossicles were found in both cases. For one sibling, the long process of the incus was described as fan-shaped and an incomplete incudostapedial joint was present. In the other case, neither crus of the stapes reached the footplate. Similarly, the findings of unilateral tympanotomy were reported for a single case of OPD syndrome by Podoshin and colleagues (1976). They reported to have observed a thickened long process of the incus and widened crura of the stapes with a normal-appearing malleus. No mobility of the ossicular chain was observed.

Characteristic audiological findings associated with OPD syndrome include mild to moderate bilateral conductive hearing loss (see Figure 3-14). For the case report by Podoshin and colleagues (1976), tympanometric findings included low compliance, absent stapedius reflexes, and a tympanometric curve characteristic of reduced mobility of the ossicular chain.

Speech

Typical cleft related problems will be associated with clefting of the palate. These include problems in childhood with sucking, swallowing, nasal regurgitation, nasal air emission, hypernasality, and the potential for compensatory articulations. Abnormal mandibular-maxillary relationships, if severe enough, might be expected to result in articulation problems involving production of bilabial, labiodental, or linguo-alveolar sounds. The presence of a conductive hearing loss may be expected to hamper the development of speech and language. The presence of mental retardation may be associated with developmental delay, poor gross motor control, learning disabilities, and school performance problems.

There are little published data related to range of severity. Because male patients typically have a cleft of the palate, whereas

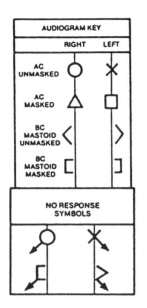

FIGURE 3–14:
Characteristic pure-tone audiometric findings associated with oto-palatal-digital syndrome.

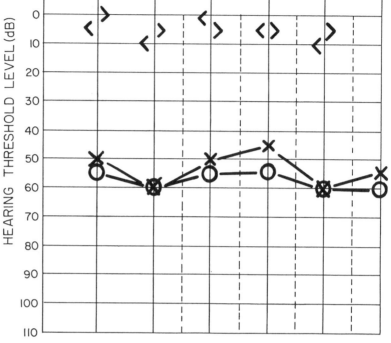

female patients do not (Gall et al., 1972), they are more prone to cleft related problems.

Management

Genetics and Medical

There appears to be a sex difference in terms of manifestations of symptoms. Gorlin, Pindborg, and Cohen (1976) stated that the syndrome is confined mainly to the male population, although affected female subjects have been reported. Three affected male subjects studied by Gall and colleagues (1972) all had cleft palate. However, none had a significant conductive hearing loss. In contrast, none of the six affected female subjects had cleft palate or "deafness." They concluded that expression of the syndrome in female subjects is mild and variable. The observations are consistent with X-linked semidominant inheritance. Male subjects with this syndrome have a 100 percent chance for carrier daughters. These daughters tend to be more mildly affected.

Female carriers have a 50 percent chance for each son to be affected and a 50 percent chance for a carrier daughter. Poznanski and colleagues (1974) demonstrated that female carriers could exhibit radiographic changes of the hands and feet. This technique could be useful in distinguishing a mildly expressing female carrier from one who does not have the gene.

Hearing

To date, attempts to restore hearing through surgical intervention have generally been unsuccessful. Surgical procedures have included stapes mobilization (Buran & Duvall, 1967) and stapedectomy (Podoshin et al., 1976). In both cases, no measureable improvement in hearing sensitivity could be documented. An excellent result could be expected from properly fitted ear level hearing aids. Frequent monitoring of the amplification program would be indicated, especially in cases with recurrent otitis media secondary to cleft palate.

Speech

Primary palatoplasty is the method of choice to treat the occurrence of a cleft palate and aid in the development of swallowing and speech activities. Secondary surgical procedures (i.e., pharyngeal flap) may be required at a later date if residual oral-nasal resonance imbalance persists. Although there are little data on the severity of mandibular malformation, surgical alteration of the mandible in severe cases of malocclusion may be expected to improve articulation performance.

Early intervention by speech pathologists and audiologists should facilitate speech and language development. Should a child show a mild intellectual impairment, close follow-up and involvement of special education professionals should be part of the treatment regimen.

Prognosis

None of the impairments associated with OPD syndrome is life threatening. The cleft palate and conductive hearing loss can be treated surgically or prosthetically. It is reasonable to assume that early diagnosis, intervention, and follow-up will be associated with a good prognosis for appropriate speech and language development.

■ References

Buran, D., & Duvall, A. (1967). The oto-palatal-digtal (OPD) syndrome. *Archives of Otolaryngology, 85,* 68–73.

Dudding, B., Gorlin, R., & Langer, L. (1967). The oto-palatal-digtal syndrome. *American Journal of Diseases of Children, 113,* 214–221.

Gall, J., Stern, A., Poznanski, A., Garn, S., Weinstein, E., & Hayward, J. (1972). Oto-palatal-digital syndrome: Comparison of clinical and radiographic manifestations in males and females. *American Journal of Human Genetics, 24,* 24–36.

Goodman, R., & Gorlin, R. (1977). *Atlas of the face in genetic disorders.* St. Louis: C. V. Mosby.

Gorlin, R., Pindborg, J., & Cohen, M. (1976). *Syndromes of the head and neck.* New York: McGraw-Hill.

Podoshin, L., Heymans, H. S., & Fradis, M. (1976). The oto-palato-digital syndrome. *Journal of Laryngology and Otology, 90,* 407–411.

Poznanski, A. K., Macpherson, R. I., Dijkman, D. J. et al. (1974). Otopalato-digital syndrome: Radiologic findings in the hand and foot. In D. Bergsma (Ed.), *Birth Defects Original Article Series, 10*(5), 125–139.

Wildervanck Syndrome
(Cervico-Oculo-Acoustic Syndrome)

■ Characteristics
Dysmorphology

With the initial delineation of cervico-oculo-acoustic syndrome by Wildervanck (1963), it has been clinically characterized by a combination of (see list):

Klippel–Feil syndrome

Duane syndrome

congenital hearing impairment

Young boy demonstrating Duane syndrome (limited abduction of the eye on lateral gaze).

The Klippel–Feil syndrome consists of cervical vertebral fusion anomalies. Severe cases result in limitation of lateral neck movement and a shorter appearing neck. The Duane syndrome is an ophthalmological condition characterized by an abducens (sixth cranial nerve) palsy which manifests as limited abduction of the eye on lateral gaze. Adduction of the eye is sometimes associated with bulbar retraction or pseudoptosis. The abducens palsy may be unilateral or bilateral.

Although Goodman and Gorlin (1977) referred to mental retardation as an associated clinical finding, there are no other reports of such in the rather sparse collection of literature pertaining to this syndrome.

Hearing

By definition, Wildervanck syndrome is characterized by hearing loss (Cremers, Hoogland, & Kuypers, 1984). The otopathology associated with this syndrome is varied and may involve the outer ear as well as the middle or inner ear (Konigsmark & Gorlin, 1976). There have been reports of preauricular tags and atresia or absence of the external auditory meatus (Fraser, 1976; Konigsmark & Gorlin, 1976). Middle ear pathology may include malformations of the malleus, congenital footplate fixation or fusion, or discontinuity of the ossicular chain (Caldarelli, 1977; Danilidis, Demetriadis, Triaridis, & Manolidis, 1980; Fraser, 1976; McLay & Maran, 1969; Singh, Rock, & Shulman, 1969). Gross malformation of the temporal bone may also occur. The cochlea may take the shape of a cyst-like structure with little evidence of a membranous labyrinth (Eisemann & Sharma, 1979; Fraser, 1976; Lindsay, 1971; McLay & Moran, 1969; Valvassori, Naunton, & Lindsay, 1969). Also the cochlea, vestibule, and semicircular canals may be contained in a single cavity (Caldarelli, 1977).

The hearing loss associated with Wildervanck syndrome can be unilateral or bilateral and the type of hearing loss may be conductive, sensorineural, or mixed (Cremers et al., 1984; Konigsmark & Gorlin, 1976). The audiometric configuration of conductive hearing losses are typically flat, and the degree of hearing loss may range from mild to moderately severe (i.e., 50 to 60 dB HL). In cases of severe histopathological anomalies of the temporal bone, the resulting hearing loss is usually profound (Baumeister & Terrahe, 1974; Palant & Carter, 1972; Schild, Mafee, & Miller, 1984; Wildervanck, Hoeksema, & Penning, 1966). Various degrees of mixed hearing loss (a combination of a conductive and a sensorineural hearing loss in the same ear) have also been reported among individuals with Wildervanck syndrome (Cremers et al., 1984; Stark & Borton, 1973). Moreover, the hearing loss may be characterized by a predominantly conductive mixed hearing loss in one ear and a predominately sensorineural mixed hearing loss in the contralateral ear (Danilidis et al., 1980).

Speech

With respect to speech and language development, the obvious debilitating feature of this syndrome is the typically severe congenital hearing loss. The magnitude of debilitation will depend on the nature of the hearing loss. Specifically, a bilateral severe sensorineural loss may be expected to seriously compromise the normal development of language and oral speech skills. A unilateral hearing loss, or a more treatable conductive hearing loss, may be expected to result in less speech and language development difficulty. The presence of vision problems may also adversely affect school performance.

Management

Genetics and Medical

This syndrome occurs almost exclusively in female individuals (Cremers et al., 1984; Eisemann & Sharma, 1979). The hearing loss is typically present at birth (Goodman & Gorlin, 1977). Although an X-linked dominant mode of inheritance has been postulated, a polygenic-multifactorial pattern with limitation to female patients is quite likely. The empirical recurrence risks for a patient's siblings or children does not seem increased above the general population. On occasion, the malformation of cervical vertebrae may need orthopedic management.

Hearing

Surgery may be contemplated in cases of middle ear pathology. However, it has been reported that improvement in hearing threshold levels following reconstructive middle ear surgery (including stapedectomy and teflon interposition) is not as successful in cases of congenital hearing disorders as in cases of otospongiosis (Cremers et al., 1984). Early (i.e., preschool) aural rehabilitation intervention programs, including the selection of hearing aids and development of communication skills, should be provided to children with Wildervanck syndrome that have a sensorineural hearing loss. Cochlear implantation is a possibility if the hearing loss consists of a profound sensorineural loss and if it is possible to verify that the auditory nerve is intact.

Speech

The extent and type of management will depend on the degree and type of involvement. In cases of bilateral severe hearing loss, present from birth, oral communication may or may not be feasible. If oral communication is not possible, stimulation using alternative means of communication (i.e., manual communication or simultaneous communication systems) may be used to facilitate communication development. If there is evidence of mental retardation, combined input from speech language pathologists and special education professionals is desirable.

Prognosis

Early communication development intervention is important, especially in cases of severe bilateral hearing losses. Unless hearing can be improved in these cases using surgery or amplification systems, the prognosis for development of oral communication is reduced. In cases of unilateral loss, the prognosis for development of normal oral communication skills is greatly improved.

■ References

Baumeister, S. K., & Terrahe, K. (1974). Innenohrmissbildugen beim Klippel–Feil syndrome. *Laryngology, Rhinology and Otology, 53,* 120–134.

Caldarelli, D. D. (1977). Congenital middle ear anomalies associated with craniofacial and skeletal syndromes. In B. B. Jaffe (Ed.), *Hearing loss children.* Baltimore: University Park Press.

Cremers, W., Hoogland, G., & Kuypers, W. (1984). Hearing loss in the cervico-oculo-acoustic (Wildervanck) syndrome. *Archives of Otolaryngology, 110,* 54–57.

Danilidis, J., Demetriadis, H., Triaridis, C., & Manolidis, L. (1980). Otological findings in cervico-oculo-auditory dysplasia. *Journal of Laryngology and Otology, 94,* 533–544.

Eisemann, M., & Sharma, G. (1979). The Wildervanck syndrome: Cervico-oculo-acoustic dysplasia. *Otolaryngology, Head and Neck Surgery, 87,* 892–897.

Fraser, G. R. (1976). *The cause of profound deafness in childhood.* Baltimore: The John Hopkins University Press.

Goodman, R., & Gorlin, R. (1977). *Atlas of the face of genetic disorders.* St. Louis: C. V. Mosby.

Konigsmark, B. W., & Gorlin, R. J. (1976). Genetic and metabolic deafness (p. 189). Philadelphia: W. B. Saunders.

Lindsay, J. R. (1971). Inner ear pathology in genetically determined congenital deafness. *Birth defects, Part IX.* Baltimore: Williams & Wilkins.

McLay, K., & Maran, A. G. C. (1969). Deafness and the Klippel–Feil syndrome. *Journal of Laryngology, 83,* 175–184.

Palant, D. I., & Carter, B. L. (1972). Klippel–Feil syndrome and deafness: A study with polytomography. *American Journal of Diseases of Children, 123,* 218–221.

Schild, J. A., Mafee, M. F., & Miller, M. F. (1984). Wildervanck syndrome: The external appearance and radiologic findings. *International Journal of Pediatric Otorhinolaryngology, 7,* 305–310.

Singh, S. P., Rock, E. H., & Shulman, A. (1969). Klippel–Feil syndrome with unexplained apparent conductive hearing loss. *Laryngoscope, 79,* 113–117.

Stark, E. W., & Borton, T. E. (1973). Klippel–Feil syndrome and associated hearing loss. *Archives of Otolarnygology, 97,* 415–419.

Valvassori, G. E., Naunton, R. F., & Lindsay, J. R. (1969). Inner ear anomalies: Clinical and histopathological considerations. *Annals of Otology, 78,* 929–936.

Wildervanck, L. S. (1963). A cervico-oculo-acusticus syndrome belonging to the status dysraphicus. *Proceedings of the 2nd International Congress of Human Genetics, Rome, 1961* (p. 1409). Rome: Instituto G. Mendel.

Wildervanck, L. S., Hoeksema, P. E., & Penning, L. (1966). Radiological examination of the inner ear of deaf-mutes presenting the cervico-oculo-acoustics syndrome. *Acta Otolaryngology, 61,* 445–453.

Chapter 4

Polygenic-Multifactorial Syndromes

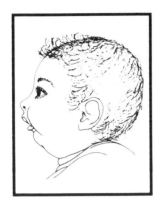

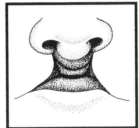

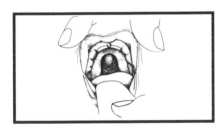

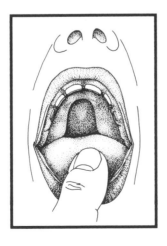

Cleft Lip and/or Cleft Palate ■

Pierre-Robin Sequence ■
(Pierre-Robin Syndrome)

Stuttering ■

Cleft Lip and/or Cleft Palate

■ Characteristics
Dysmorphology

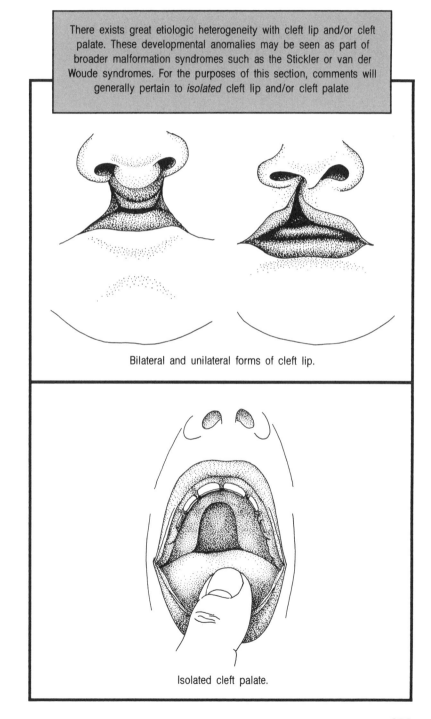

There exists great etiologic heterogeneity with cleft lip and/or cleft palate. These developmental anomalies may be seen as part of broader malformation syndromes such as the Stickler or van der Woude syndromes. For the purposes of this section, comments will generally pertain to *isolated* cleft lip and/or cleft palate

Bilateral and unilateral forms of cleft lip.

Isolated cleft palate.

Frequency of occurrence of cleft lip with or without cleft palate ranges from .8 to 1.6 per 1,000 live births (Fraser, 1971). Isolated cleft palate occurs less frequently in Caucasians (.45 per 1,000) than does cleft lip with or without cleft palate. Cleft lip with or without cleft palate occurs with higher frequency in Caucasians (1.34 per 1,000) than in Blacks (0.41 per 1,000) and higher in Asians (2.13 per 1,000) and certain North American Indians than in Caucasians. Cleft palate alone is represented by occurrence of .4 per 1,000 for Blacks, .48 for Caucasians, and .55 for Asians (Chung & Myrianthopoulos, 1968; Fraser, 1971; Miller, 1963; Neel, 1958; Oka, 1979). For both isolated cleft lip and palate, the incidence in male subjects is much larger (62 percent) than for female subjects (38 percent) (Oka, 1979). For cleft palate alone, the ratios are quite different. Oka (1979) noted that the incidence for female subjects is 57 percent whereas male subjects have a 43 percent occurrence of isolated cleft palate.

Hearing

Reported incidence of hearing loss among individuals with a cleft lip with or without a cleft palate vary considerably (Bluestone, 1978). In general, investigators report that hearing disorders are observed in 50 to 100 percent of individuals with a cleft palate (Bergstrom, 1978; Bluestone, 1978; Downs, Jafec, & Wood, 1981; Mattucci, 1979; Northern & Downs, 1984; Siedentop, 1977). Siedentop (1977) reported that 90 percent of children under age one who have a cleft palate display significant pathologic middle ear problems. Mattucci (1979) reported that 50 percent of individuals with a cleft palate have hearing disorders that persist into adulthood.

Sensorineural hearing loss has been reported among a small proportion of individuals with cleft palate (Bergstrom, 1978). However, conductive hearing loss is by far the most prevalent type of hearing loss associated with cleft palate and cleft lip. Anomalies in the muscles involved in Eustachian tube function (including the tensor veli palatini and levator veli palatini) are the primary cause of middle ear disease observed among individuals with cleft lip or cleft palate (Bluestone, 1978; Paradise, 1980). The middle ear diseases most often reported among this population include serous, acute, and chronic otitis media (McWilliams, Morris, & Shelton, 1984). If left untreated, the otitis media may develop into additional hearing pathologies, including perforation of the tympanic membrane, tympanosclerosis, ossicular discontinuity, fixation of the ossicular chain, cholesteatoma, mastoiditis, labyrinthitis, and facial paralysis (Bluestone et al., 1983).

The degree of hearing loss associated with otitis media can vary from subclinical to a moderate hearing loss (i.e., approximately 50 dB HL). Average pure tone thresholds in the range of 20 to 30 dB HL are the rule (Bluestone, Beery, & Paradise, 1973; Kokko,

1975). Typically, the hearing loss is characterized by a flat or a gently rising audiometric configuration (i.e., better threshold levels at high frequencies).

Speech

The primary problems affecting individuals with cleft lip or palate relate to communication skills affecting language, speech, resonance and voice production, and hearing (McWilliams et al., 1984).

Children born with cleft lip or palate often show difficulties with feeding, sucking, and swallowing because of the separation of the oral pharyngeal and nasal cavities. Overt clefts may be recognized during birth, whereas submucous clefts of the hard or soft palate may only become obvious with feeding problems or failure to thrive.

Poor hearing, late palatal closure, and poor speech and language stimulation from caregivers in the environment may lead to delays in oral language development and poor early speech skills. In addition, resonance imbalance (hypernasality) may occur when the oral-nasal contrasts for speech are ineffective because of the lack of efficient velopharyngeal closure. The combination of poor hearing and lack of adequate velopharyngeal closure may lead the child to develop compensatory patterns of articulation which substitute back of the tongue sounds (glottal stops, pharyngeal fricatives) for front of mouth sounds (bilabial, linguo-alveolar stops or fricatives). In addition, the inability to effect good velopharyngeal closure may dictate that the child produce larger amounts of subglottal air pressure and a tighter vocal fold closure in order to achieve a vocal output that matches other voices heard in the environment. This overdriving of the laryngeal mechanism may lead to vocal abuse or misuse and an increased risk for vocal fold lesions, such as vocal nodules. The poor ability to monitor receptive information due to reduced hearing levels (prevalent Eustachian tube and middle ear problems) may account for the delays seen in listening vocabulary, grammatical marker differences, morphophonemic difficulties, and reduced attention to the incoming communication message. In addition, verbal output may be reduced in amount and complexity as hearing and oral motor efficiency is reduced. With such input and output problems apparent, many of these children show language learning difficulties in the early school years and inappropriate social language usage (pragmatics) in the later school years (McWilliams et al., 1984).

Management

Genetics and Medical

It has generally been accepted that cleft lip with or without cleft of the palate is etiologically and genetically different from isolated clefts of the palate. Much of the published data deal with clefts of the lip and palate, whereas relatively little data are available for isolated clefts of the palate. What is known about individuals with cleft palate alone is that they suffer from a higher incidence (24 percent) (Green, Vermillion, Hay, Gibbens, & Kerschbaum, 1964) of other congenital anomalies compared to persons with cleft lip and palate (14 percent) or cleft lip alone (seven percent).

Genetically, the factors underlying cleft lip and palate may include (1) mutant genes, (2) chromosomal aberrations, (3) environmental teratogens, and (4) polygenic-multifactorial inheritance. It appears that a majority of individuals with isolated cleft lip and palate fall into the latter category (Fraser, 1971).

A polygenic-multifactorial developmental threshold model can be used to explain cleft of the secondary palate. It is thought that in order to close, the palatal shelves must reorient themselves from a vertical position on either side of the tongue to a horizontal plane above the tongue where their medial edges meet and fuse. During the time of reorientation, the head continues to grow, carrying the base of the shelves farther apart. If the shelves become horizontal too late, the head will be so big that the shelves will be unable to meet and a cleft palate will result. The latest point in development when the shelves can reach the horizontal and still meet can be considered a threshold.

In the case of cleft palate, many factors can influence the stage in which the shelves move to the horizontal. These factors include:

■ the force within the shelves that promotes their movement to the horizontal
■ the size of the tongue
■ the timing of palatal shelf reorientation
■ the size of the space needed to be closed over (dependent upon the width of the face and other factors)

Each of these is influenced by environmental and genetic factors. This, then, follows a polygenic-multifactorial model of inheritance.

As with most conditions due to polygenic-multifactorial inheritance, it is most often observed as a single case within a family. Given a thorough evaluation by a clinical geneticist to rule out a syndromic diagnosis or environmental teratogen, the empiric recurrence risks are relatively low. Table 4–1, 4–2, and 4–3 are empiric risk figures which take into consideration the degree of relatedness, the proband's sex, and the severity of the cleft.

Hearing

Because the prevalence of otitis media is high among this population, all individuals with a cleft lip or palate should be pro-

TABLE 4–1
Recurrence Risks for Cleft Lip with and without Cleft Palate

Relation to Proband	Risk
Sibs	3–4%
Children	3–5%
Aunts and uncles	0.6–0.8%
Nieces and nephews	0.7–0.8%
First cousins	0.2–0.4%
General population	0.1%

TABLE 4–2
Recurrence in Relation to Proband's Sex

Type of Cleft	Sex	Approximate % Sibs Affected
Cleft lip with or without cleft palate	M	4%
	F	5%
Cleft palate only	M	6%
	F	2–3%

TABLE 4–3
Recurrence in Relation to Severity of Cleft in Cleft Lip/Cleft Palate

Type of Cleft	% Affected
Bilateral with or without cleft palate	5–6%
Unilateral with or without cleft palate	4%
Unilateral cleft lip	2–3%

vided with a comprehensive otological management program (Heller, 1979; Hunter & Klein, 1979). Audiological evaluations including air conduction and bone conduction threshold as well as immittance audiometry should be completed every three to six months (Bess, Lewis, & Cieliczka, 1979; Downs et al., 1981; McWilliams et al., 1984).

The most common otological treatments for otitis media include the prescription of antimicrobial medication (Paradise, 1980) and myringotomy with insertion of tympanotomy tubes (Garrard & Clark, 1985). Hearing aids should be considered in cases of prolonged recurrent otitis media, especially when there is evidence that the child displays significant speech or language delays (Downs et al., 1981). Finally, parents of children with a cleft lip/ cleft palate should be taught to recognize the early signs of hearing loss and otitis media. Furthermore, they should be informed of the importance of seeking medical attention to treat the disease (McWilliams et al., 1984).

Speech

This group of individuals typically follows the traditional path for surgical, dental, and behavioral management of the associated craniofacial problems. Surgery to close the lip is usually completed at about 3 months of age, with the palate surgically closed at about 12 to 14 months of age (McWilliams et al., 1984). During the first several months of life, dental appliances may be used to cover the hard palate for alignment of the alveolar segments to improve surgical continuity of the lip and anterior dental arch (Latham, 1980) and to act as a temporary artificial palate to aid in feeding and swallowing. The prosthetic separation of the oral and nasal cavities is also seen as a positive step in aiding oral-nasal phonemic contrasts for normal speech development. For many persons, primary surgery eliminates the potential for developing abnormal resonance balance (hypernasality, nasal air emission) by virtue of obtaining an efficient velopharyngeal port system. Thus, articulation development may proceed at a more normal pace without abnormal posterior positioning of the tongue for development of glottal stops and fricatives and pharyngeal stops and fricative elements frequently seen in children with an incompetent velopharyngeal mechanism. In certain cases where other problems exist within the child (i.e., intermittent hearing loss, poor speech and language stimulation, cognitive deficits), direct speech and language therapy and parent training programs designed to foster speech and language stimulation at home are necessary.

As the child grows, more comprehensive evaluations of several aspects of language competency and usage should be considered. Some children with cleft lip or cleft palate are at risk for language learning disabilities that will affect school performance. Comprehensive language and psychoeducational testing during the primary school years may aid in planning special programs for these children and may prevent systematic failure in oral and written language growth so necessary for success in secondary school years (McWilliams et al., 1984).

Prognosis

Mental development is expected to follow the distribution seen in the normal population.

In general, the incidence and severity of hearing problems associated with cleft lip or cleft palate tend to diminish with advances in age from childhood to adulthood (Northern & Downs, 1984; Siedentop, 1977). However, with aggressive audiological and otological treatment, the occurrence of otitis media can be controlled effectively.

In general, prognosis for developing speech and language within general normal limits is good. Certain individuals who only have cleft palates (especially male patients) are more at risk for speech, hearing, and language and learning problems. Early intervention and management will aid the child in reaching his or her potential (McWilliams et al., 1984).

■ References

Bergstrom, L. (1978). Congenital and acquired deafness in clefting and craniofacial syndromes. *Cleft Palate Journal, 15,* 254–261.

Bess, T., Lewis, H., & Cieliczka, D. (1975). Acoustic impedance measurements in cleft-palate children. *Journal of Speech and Hearing Disorders, 40,* 13–22.

Bluestone, C. C. (1978). Prevalence and pathogenesis of ear disease and hearing loss. In M. D. Graham (Ed.), *Cleft palate: Middle ear disease and hearing loss.* Springfield, IL: Charles C. Thomas.

Bluestone, C. D., Beery, Q. C., & Paradise, J. L. (1973). Audiometry and tympanometry in relation to middle ear effusions in children. *Laryngoscope, 83,* 594–604.

Bluestone, C. D., Klein, J. O., Paradise, J. L., et al. (1983). Workshop in effects of otitis media on the child. *Pediatrics, 71,* 639–649.

Chung, C. S., & Myrianthopoulos, N. C. (1968). Racial and prenatal factors in major congenital malformations. *American Journal of Human Genetics, 20,* 44–60.

Downs, M. P., Jafek, B., & Wood, R. P., II. (1981). Comprehensive treatment of children with recurrent serous otitis media. *Otolaryngology, Head and Neck Surgery, 89,* 658–665.

Fraser, F. C. (1971). Etiology of cleft lip and palate. In W. C. Grabb, S. R. Rosenstein, & K. R. Bzoch (Eds.), *Cleft lip and palate* (pp. 54–65). Boston: Little, Brown and Company.

Garrard, K. R., & Clark, B. (1985). Otitis media: The role of speech-language pathologists. *American Speech and Hearing Association, 27,* 35–39.

Green, J. C., Vermillion, J. R., Hay, S., Gibbens, S. F., & Kerschbaum, S. (1964). Epidemiologic study of cleft lip and cleft palate in four states. *Journal of the American Dental Association, 68,* 387–404.

Heller, J. C. (1979). Hearing loss in patients with cleft palate. In K. Bzoch (Ed.), *Communicative disorders related to cleft lip and cleft palate.* Boston: Little, Brown and Company.

Hunter, D., & Klein, R. (1979). Detection of middle ear disease in cleft-palate patients. *Otolaryngology, Head and Neck Surgery, 87,* 876–879.

Kokko, E. (1975). Chronic secretory otitis media in children. *Acta Otolaryngologica, 327,* 7–44.

Latham, R. (1980). Orthopaedic advancement of the cleft maxillary segment: A preliminary report. *Cleft Palate Journal, 27,* 227–233.

Mattucci, K. F. (1979). Cleft palate patient: Otologic management. *New York State Journal of Medicine, 79,* 333–339.

McWilliams, B., Morris, H., & Shelton, R. (1984). *Cleft palate speech.* Philadelphia: B. C. Decker Inc.

Miller, J. R. (1963). The use of registries and vital statistics in the study of malformations. *Second International Congress on Congenital Malformation,* 334. New York.

Neel, J. V. (1958). A study of major congenital defects in Japanese infants. *Journal of Human Genetics, 10,* 398–445.

Northern, J. L., & Downs, M. P. (1984). *Hearing in children* (3rd ed.). Baltimore: Williams & Wilkins.

Oka, S. W. (1979). Epidemiology and genetics of clefting: With implications for etiology. In H. K. Cooper, R. L. Harding, W. M. Krogman, M. Mazaheri, & R. T. Millard (Eds.), *Cleft palate and cleft lip: A team approach to clinical management and rehabilitation of the patient.* Philadelphia: W. B. Saunders.

Paradise, J. L. (1980). Otitis media in infants and children. *Pediatrics, 65,* 917–943.

Siedentop, K. H. (1977). Eustachian tube function. In B. F. Jaffe (Ed.), *Hearing loss in children* (pp. 381–396). Baltimore: University Park Press.

Pierre-Robin Sequence
(Pierre-Robin Syndrome)

■ **Characteristics**
Dysmorphology

mandibular hypoplasia

glossoptosis

cleft of the soft palate

Pierre-Robin sequence can be etiologically thought of as an error in development in which the initial defect is mandibular hypoplasia. Secondarily, glossoptosis and cleft of the soft palate result (Dennison, 1965; Peterson-Falzone, 1981). Thus, the sequence of developmental anomalies includes (see list):

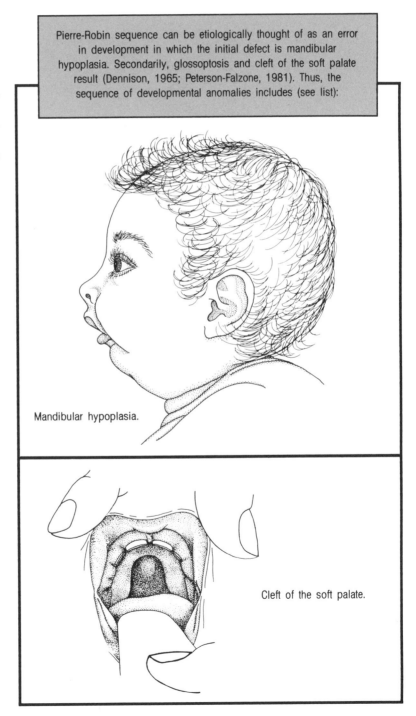

Mandibular hypoplasia.

Cleft of the soft palate.

The mandibular hypoplasia may be the result of genetic factors or secondary to in utero constraint causing compression of the mandible and limitation of growth. It is hypothesized that posterior and upward displacement of the tongue impairs closure of the palatal shelves, with clefting a subsequent feature of this developmental sequence (Latham, 1966). If clefting is present, it may vary from a bifid uvula to a wide U-shaped cleft palate. This latter finding differs from the inverted V-shaped cleft palates usually seen as a result of malformation. Cleft palates due to an intrinsic developmental problem are also less likely to be associated with micrognathia or glossoptosis. As the clefting of the Pierre-Robin sequence is a secondary result of the micrognathia, it is not seen in association with cleft lip (Gorlin, Pindborg, & Cohen, 1976).

The Pierre-Robin sequence may be an isolated finding or occur as part of a broader syndromic diagnosis (Pashayan & Lewis, 1984). For example, Stickler syndrome is often referred to as a pedigree of Pierre-Robin sequence (Schreiner, McAlister, Marshall, & Shearer, 1973). Goodman and Gorlin (1977) stated that the combination of cleft palate, micrognathia, and glossoptosis is a nonspecific symptom complex which may occur in a variety of disorders.

Hearing

Anomalies of the ears and hearing loss have been reported among individuals with Pierre-Robin sequence. Physical anomalies of the external and middle ears include deformed pinnae, low set ears, unusual angle of the external auditory meatus, and structural defects of the middle ear ossicles (Pashayan & Lewis, 1984; Peterson, 1977; Peterson-Falzone, 1981). Igarashi, Filippone, and Alford (1976) reported temporal bone deformities in an infant with Pierre-Robin sequence. Although infrequent, cases of sensorineural hearing loss associated with Pierre-Robin sequence have been reported (Pashayan & Lewis, 1984; Peterson, 1977).

Otitis media caused by cleft palate is the most frequent cause of hearing loss observed in Pierre-Robin sequence. Conductive hearing loss with air conduction pure-tone averages ranging from 20 to 30 dB HL are common among individuals with cleft palate (Bluestone, Beery, & Paradise, 1973; Kokko, 1975). The hearing loss may be unilateral or bilateral (Pashayan & Lewis, 1984). Typically, the hearing loss is characterized by a flat or a slightly rising audiometric configuration.

Speech

Potential speech and language development problems are those typically associated with clefting and related hearing loss. Palatopharyngeal valving problems due to unrepaired cleft or velopharyngeal inadequacy may be expected to result in nasal regurgitation of food or liquids, nasal air emission, hypernasality, and abnormal compensatory articulation patterns. Language development may be delayed because of hearing loss and possibly frequent hospitalizations. Articulation development may be hampered by the severe mandibular underdevelopment.

Pashayan and Lewis (1984) compared some speech and language aspects of subjects with isolated Pierre-Robin sequence to those with the sequence as part of a syndrome. In the isolated group of 17 subjects, 6 had either receptive or expressive language delays, 4 had articulation problems, and 1 exhibited velopharyngeal inadequacy. In the syndrome group of 8 subjects, 7 had either receptive or expressive language delays, 6 had articulation problems, and 1 had velopharyngeal inadequacy.

Management

Genetics and Medical

The immediate concern in the newborn period is whether upper airway obstruction may occur as a result of tongue positioning. Prompt attention to securing an adequate upper airway decreases the chance of hypoxic damage. Genetic counseling and prognosis will depend on the exact cause of the Pierre-Robin sequence. If it is part of the Stickler syndrome, autosomal dominant genetic factors are presumed operative. Association with severe syndromes such as trisomy 18 are unlikely to pose significant recurrence risks to parents as long as familial chromosomal factors (i.e., balanced translocations) are not present in either parent. In isolated cases, where a syndromic diagnosis has been ruled out, the empirical recurrence risks are probably low (approximately 5 percent).

Hearing

The incidence of hearing loss among individuals with cleft palate is elevated (Downs, Jafek, & Wood, 1981; Mattucci, 1979). Thus, individuals with Pierre-Robin sequence who have a cleft palate should be provided with a comprehensive otological and audiological management program (refer to the previous section on cleft lip/cleft palate). Myringotomies and tympanotomy tubes appear to be the treatment of choice for individuals with Pierre-Robin sequence who suffer from otitis media (Pashayan & Lewis, 1984).

Speech

After upper airway and feeding problems are managed, the palatal cleft (Peterson-Falzone, 1981) needs surgical consideration. The Douglas procedure may be used to keep the tongue tip forward in an attempt to avoid airway blockage (Smith & Stowe, 1961). Although surgical correction of micrognathia has been attempted, it is felt that this condition improves with age in the absence of surgery. The improvement is especially noticeable in those cases in which the micrognathia is due to in utero compression.

After the palatal defect has been closed using surgical and/or prosthetic means, management may follow regimens typically employed in cases of cleft palate and associated hearing loss.

Prognosis

Prognosis for survival relates primarily to the success of airway management in the infant. Pashayan and Lewis (1984) and Goodman and Gorlin (1977) suggested a good prognosis for normal growth and development if the patient survives infancy. Pashayan and Lewis (1984) assigned a poorer prognosis to patients exhibiting the Pierre-Robin sequence as part of a syndrome. With respect to speech and language development, prognosis will depend on the severity and success of surgical and behavioral management techniques. The earlier and more comprehensive the management, the better the prognosis.

■ References

Bluestone, C. D., Beery, Q. C., & Paradise, J. L. (1973). Audiometry and tympanometry in relation to middle ear effusions in children. *Laryngoscope, 83,* 594–604.

Dennison, W. (1965). The Pierre Robin syndrome. *Pediatrics, 36,* 336–341.

Downs, M. P., Jafek, B., & Wood, R. P., II. (1981). Comprehensive treatment of children with recurrent serous otitis media. *Otolaryngology, Head and Neck Surgery, 89,* 658–665.

Goodman, R., & Gorlin, R. (1977). *Atlas of the face in genetic disorders.* St. Louis: C. V. Mosby.

Gorlin, R., Pindborg, J., & Cohen, M. (1976). *Syndromes of the head and neck.* New York: McGraw-Hill.

Igarashi, M., Filippone, M., & Alford, B. (1976). Temporal bone findings in Pierre Robin syndrome. *Laryngoscope, 86,* 1679–1687.

Kokko, E. (1975). Chronic secretory otitis media in children. *Acta Otolaryngology, 327,* 7–44.

Latham, R. A. (1966). The pathogenesis of cleft palate associated with Pierre Robin syndrome. *British Journal of Plastic Surgery, 19,* 205.

Mattucci, K. F. (1979). Cleft palate patient: Otologic management. *New York State Journal of Medicine, 79,* 333–339.

Pashayan, H., & Lewis, M. (1984). Clinical experience with the Robin sequence. *Cleft Palate Journal, 21,* 270–276.

Peterson, R. A. (1977). Ophthalmology. In B. F. Jaffe (Ed.), *Hearing loss in children* (pp. 228–240). Baltimore: University Park Press.

Peterson-Falzone, S. J. (19810. Impact of communicative disorders on otolaryngologic care of patients with craniofacial anomalies. *Otolaryn-*

gologic Clinics of North America, 14, 895–915.

Schreiner, R., McAlister, W., Marshall, R., & Shearer, W. (1973). Stickler syndrome in a pedigree of Pierre Robin syndrome. *American Journal of Diseases of Children, 126,* 86–90.

Smith, J., & Stowe, F. (1961). The Pierre Robin syndrome (glossoptosis, micrognathia, cleft palate). *Pediatrics, 27,* 128–133.

Stuttering

■ Characteristics
Dysmorphology

sound and syllable repetitions (part-word repetitions)

word repetitions

sound prolongations

tense pauses or hesitations

interjections

Unlike the majority of syndromes described in this text, stuttering is not characterized by specific physical features. It is a speech disorder frequently accompanied by concomitant physical behaviors and by fears and negative attitudes toward speaking. It is defined in the *International Classification of Diseases* (p. 202), as "disorders in the rhythm of speech, in which the individual knows precisely what he wishes to say, but at the time is unable to say it because of an involuntary repetitive prolongation or cessation of a sound" (World Health Organization, 1977). Speech characteristics may include (see list):

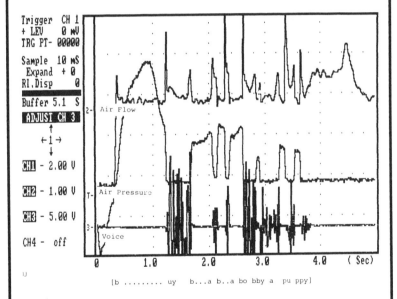

[b .... uy   b...a b..a bo bby a   pu ppy]

Aerodynamic characterization of the phrase "Buy Bobby a Puppy" produced by a stutterer. Notice that there is a large amount of intra-oral air pressure buildup on the /b/ in "Buy". This also increases the duration of the closure duration on the sound before it is released. In addition, there are repetitions of the /b/ + vowel /a/ in word "Bobby" which also show increased air pressure and increased duration. Air flow released following the large buildup of air pressure may also be seen as high in "Buy" and "Bobby".

Concomitant or secondary behaviors may include:

- loss of eye contact
- eye blinking
- head or body jerks
- facial grimaces
- tension and tremor
- audible inhalation

The fears and negative attitudes that may accompany the disorder may be evident in such behaviors as disguise reactions, word substitution and circumlocution, and situation avoidance (Bloodstein, 1981; Johnson, 1959, 1961; Van Riper, 1982; Wingate, 1964).

Age of onset is typically between two and five, with the median age about four (Andrews, Criag, Feyer, Hoddinot, Howie, & Neilson; Andrews & Harris, 1964). The prevalence of stuttering is estimated to be one percent, whereas the incidence, or lifetime risk of stuttering, is four to five percent (Andrews et al., 1983; Bloodstein, 1981; Van Riper, 1982).

Numerous theories concerning the causes of the disorder have been proposed, describing stuttering as neurotic behavior, learned behavior, or a physiological disorder (Andrews et al., 1983; Van Riper, 1982). More specifically, investigators have studied the link between stuttering and environmental factors, auditory function, central nervous system characteristics, language development, and motor programming factors, to name a few (Andrews et al., 1983; Curlee & Perkins, 1984). There is evidence that the laryngeal behavior of stutterers differs from that of nonstutterers (Adams, Freeman, & Conture, 1984). Results in many of these areas of investigation are inconsistent, leading to the speculation that stutterers do not form a homogeneous population, but may be divided into subgroups.

Genetics

Stuttering is more common in male subjects than female subjects, the ratio being approximately three to one (Bloodstein, 1981; Kidd, Kidd, & Records, 1978). The risk of stuttering is greater for relatives of stutterers than for the general population. This susceptibility to stuttering is also affected by the sex of the proband and the sex of the relative, with male relatives of female stutterers being at greatest risk (Andrews et al, 1983; Andrews & Harris, 1964; Kidd, 1984; Kidd, Heimbuch, & Records, 1981).

Studies of familial concentration, the sex ratio, and incidence in twins have led to investigation of a genetic component in stuttering. Data obtained in the Yale Family Study of Stuttering indicate that susceptibility to stuttering does follow a pattern of vertical transmission with sex-modified expression (Kidd, 1984; Kidd et al., 1981). However, stuttering may not be accounted for entirely by genetic models, and many authors now suggest that the disorder may be the result of a gene-environment interaction (Curlee & Perkins, 1984; Kidd, 1984).

Management

Management of incipient stutterering in young children usually involves parent counseling concerning modification of environmental factors that may exacerbate the problem. The nature and severity of the disfluency, as well as the child's reaction to it, may determine the extent of direct intervention with the child.

Current treatment procedures for older children and adults have been described by Curlee and Perkins (1984), Guitar and Peters (1982), and others as belonging to one of two different approaches. The goal of one approach is to establish or shape fluency, whereas the second focuses on management or modification of stuttering.

Fluency shaping programs are highly behavioral in nature, and involve the establishment, generalization, and maintenance of a new, fluent speech pattern. Most incorporate the use of a prolonged speech technique, which is sometimes established through the use of delayed auditory feedback. Outcome studies indicate that prolonged speech techniques have both short- and long-term effectiveness (Andrews, Guitar, & Howie, 1980; Howie & Andrews, 1984). However, as the fluent speech of treated stutterers can be distinguished from that of nonstutterers, the establishment of speech naturalness has been the focus of recent discussion and research (Onslow & Ingham, 1987).

Stuttering modification therapies may also incorporate behavioral techniques to enable the stutterer to manage the moment of stuttering. However, greater emphasis is placed on confronting and managing the fears and attitudes associated with the disorder.

Other approaches to the treatment of stuttering have included the use of biofeedback, hypnosis, drug regimens, and masking (Ingham, 1984). Although these may be useful adjuncts to therapy, none have proven long-term effectiveness (Ingham, 1984).

Prognosis

There is, to date, no cure for stuttering. However, spontaneous recovery in children is common and the probability of recovery by age 16 has been estimated at 78 percent (Andrews et al., 1983).

As most current therapies involve behavior change, a maintenance phase is a critical aspect of any treatment program. Relapse following therapy may occur in as many as one-third of clients treated (Martin, 1981). Treatment of children may produce more long lasting results (Curlee & Perkins, 1984).

■ References

Adams, M. R., Freeman, F. J., & Conture, E. G. (1984). Laryngeal dynamics of stutterers. In R. F. Curlee & W. H. Perkins (Eds.), *Nature and treatment of stuttering: New directions.* San Diego: College-Hill Press.

Andrews, G., Craig, A., Feyer, A-M., Hoddinot, S., Howie, P., & Neilson, M. (1983). Stuttering: A review of research findings and theories circa 1982. *Journal of Speech and Hearing Disorders, 18,* 226–246.

Andrews, G., Guitar, B., & Howie, P. (1980). Meta-analysis of the effects of stuttering treatment. *Journal of Speech and Hearing Disorders, 45,* 287–309.

Andrews, G., & Harris, M. (1964). *The syndrome of stuttering* (Clinics in develomental medicine No. 17). London: Heinemann.

Bloodstein, O. (1981). *A handbook on stuttering.* Chicago: National Easter Seal Society.

Curlee, R. F., & Perkins, W. H. (Eds.). (1984). *Nature and treatment of stuttering: New directions.* San Diego: College-Hill Press.

Guitar, B., & Peters, T. J. (1982). *Stuttering: An integration of contemporary therapies.* Memphis, TN: Speech Foundation of America.

Howie, P., & Andrews, G. (1984). Treatment of adults. Managing fluency. In R. F. Curlee & W. H. Perkins (Eds.), *Nature and treatment of stuttering: New directions.* San Diego: College-Hill Press.

Ingham, R. J. (1984). *Stuttering and behavior therapy: Current status and experimental foundations.* San Diego: College-Hill Press.

Johnson, W. (1959). *The onset of stuttering.* Minneapolis: University of Minnesota Press.

Johnson, W. (1961). Measurements of oral reading and speaking rate and disfluency of adult male and female stutterers and non-stutterers. *Journal of Speech and Hearing Disorders* (Monograph Suppl. 7), 1–20.

Kidd, K. K. (1984). Stuttering as a genetic disorder. In R. F. Curlee & W. H. Perkins (Eds.), *Nature and treatment of stuttering: New directions.* San Diego: College-Hill Press.

Kidd, K. K., Heimbuch, R. C., & Records, M. A. (1981). Vertical transmission of susceptibility to stuttering with sex-modified expression. *Proceedings of the National Academy of Sciences, 78,* 606–610.

Kidd, K. K., Kidd, J. R., & Records, M. A. (1978). The possible causes of the sex ratio in stuttering and its implications. *Journal of Fluency Disorders, 3,* 13–23.

Martin, R. R. (1981). Introduction and perspective: Review of published research. In E. Boberg (Ed.), *Maintenance of fluency.* New York: Elsevier North Holland.

Onslow, M., & Ingham, R. J. (1987). Speech quality measurement and the management of stuttering. *Journal of Speech and Hearing Disorders, 52,* 2–17.

Van Riper, C. (1982). *The nature of stuttering.* Englewood Cliffs, NJ: Prentice Hall.

Wingate, M. E. (1964). A standard definition of stuttering. *Journal of Speech and Hearing Disorders, 29,* 484–489.

World Health Organization. (1977). *Manual of the international statistical classification of diseases, injuries and causes of death* (Vol. 1). Geneva: Author.

Chapter 5

Sporadic Syndromes

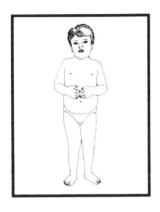

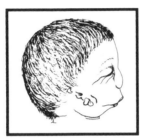

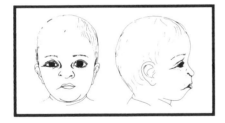

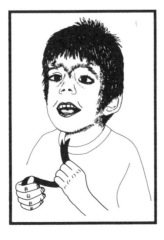

Cornelia de Lange Syndrome ■
(de Lange Syndrome;
Brachman-de Lange Syndrome)

Goldenhar Syndrome ■
(Oculoauriculovertebral Dysplasia;
First and Second
Branchial Arch Syndrome;
Hemifacial Microsomia)

Moebius Syndrome ■
(Congenital Facial Diplegia)

Prader-Willi Syndrome ■
(Prader-Labhart-Willi Syndrome)

Cornelia de Lange Syndrome
(de Lange Syndrome; Brachman-de Lange Syndrome)

■ Characteristics
Dysmorphology

prenatal onset of
growth retardation

microcephaly

mental retardation

confluent eyebrows/hirsutism

anteverted nares/small nose

downturned upper lip

small extremities with
occasional phocomelia
or oligodactly

severe language and
speech problems

hearing loss

Brachman (1916) and de Lange (1933) independently described
Cornelia de Lange syndrome, which features (see list):

Features of Cornelia de Lange syndrome include hirsutism, microcephaly,
confluent eyebrows, and a small nose with anteverted nares.

The degree of developmental delay is usually severe. Medical problems may also be complex, owing to the multiple organ systems that may be involved.

Hearing

The otological and audiological manifestations of Cornelia de Lange syndrome are not well documented. Anomalies of the external ear are often reported. The malformations include low set auricles, large pinnae, small external auditory canals, and irregularly slanted outer canals (Fraser & Campbell, 1978; Hersh et al., 1985; Jervis & Stimson, 1963; McIntire & Eisen, 1965; Silver, 1964; Smith, Berg, & McCreary, 1969). In a case presentation of a patient with Cornelia de Lange syndrome, Silver (1964) reported a significant hearing loss. Moreover, the author stated that "apparent deafness" was observed in several individuals with Cornelia de Lange syndrome. However, no audiological information was provided. McIntire and Eisen (1965) reported a case study of a child with Cornelia de Lange syndrome who displayed a mild conductive hearing loss at the low frequencies and a moderate bilateral sensorineural hearing loss at high frequencies.

Speech

The variety of anomalies of the oral-facial region is large and may contribute to some degree of speech problems in these patients. However, the degree of mental retardation in these patients is the major factor in the severe delays of both receptive and expressive language development. The rough vocal quality appears to continue in later life and may be a part of the systemic changes that have occurred to the larynx and pharynx. Thus mental age–consistent speech and language appears to be the observed characteristics of affected persons studied to date (Fraser & Campbell, 1978; Moore, 1970).

Management

Genetics and Medical

Most cases appear to be of sporadic occurrence. Robinson, Wolfsberg, and Jones (1985) indicated that the syndrome may be inherited in an autosomal dominant fashion. They suggested that the apparent sporadic nature in otherwise normal families might represent the reduced ability of severely affected persons to reproduce.

Numerous investigations have noted a higher incidence of chromosomal aberrations in patients with a Cornelia de Lange-like syndrome phenotype. However, a small group of patients exhibiting the characteristic syndrome complex did not have demonstrable chromosome changes by specialized chromosome banding techniques (Breslau, Disteche, Hall, Thuline, & Cooper, 1981). This suggests that there is probable etiologic heterogeneity in this phenotype. Some chromosomal syndromes such as duplication of the long arm of number 3 (3q+) have overlapping clinical features. This may be due to the observed growth retardation in many chromosomal syndromes resulting in hirsutism, microcephaly, and severe retardation. Chromosomal investigations are indicated to help in ruling out those similar entities.

In the absence of a positive family history, the empirical recurrence risk is in the one to three percent range (Smith et al., 1969).

Medical problems such as congenital heart disease can increase the susceptibility to infectious diseases. Careful assessments of the eyes, heart, and gastrointestinal tract may be indicated if related signs or symptoms should develop. Any seizure activity also needs prompt attention and management.

Speech

As speech and language delays are severe, therapy should begin as soon as a diagnosis is made. General language stimulation employing a parent language teaching format would be useful. Given the significant hearing loss that has been reported in some of these individuals (Silver, 1964), careful aural management should have a positive effect on speech and language development. Individual therapy for these children should focus on developing receptive and expressive vocabulary and syntax appropriate for mental age. Later stages of language training should concentrate on pragmatic skills according to environmental needs and cognitive abilities (Moore, 1970).

Prognosis

Overall, survival is much reduced with severe limitation of developmental potential. With speech and language development, prognosis is obviously dependent upon the cognitive level of functioning of the individual. Because severe retardation has been found in a large percentage of patients with Cornelia de Lange syndrome, expectations for normal speech and language abilities are poor. Careful monitoring of hearing function and early speech and language stimulation by parents and professionals will allow the individuals to attain maximum potential.

■ References

Brachmann, W. (1916). Ein Fall von symmetrischer Monodaktylie durch Ulna-defekt, mit symmetrischer Flughautbildung in den Ellenbogen sowie anderen Abnormalitaten. *JB Kinderheilk Phys Erzieh, 84,* 224–235.

Breslau, E. J., Disteche, C., Hall, J. G., Thuline, H., & Cooper, P. (1981). Prometaphase chromosomes in five patients with the Brachmann-de Lange syndrome. *American Journal of Medical Genetics, 10,* 179–186.

de Lange, C. (1933). Sur un type noveau de degeneration (typus Amstelodemensis). *Archives Medical Enfants, 36,* 713–719.

Fraser, W. I., & Campbell, B. M. (1978). A study of six cases of de Lange Amsterdam syndrome, with special attention to voice, speech and language characteristics. *Developmental Medicine and Child Neurology, 20,* 189–198.

Hersh, J. J., Dale, K. S., Gerald, P. S., Yen, F. F., Weisskopf, B., & Dinno, N. D. (1985). Dup(4p)del(9p) in a familial mental retardation syndrome. *American Journal of Diseases of Children, 139,* 81–84.

Jervis, G. A., & Stimson, C. W. (1963). De Lange syndrome. *Journal of Pediatrics, 63,* 634–645.

McIntire, M. S., & Eisen, J. D. (1965). de Lange syndrome. *Birth Defects, 5,* 18–21.

Moore, M. V. (1970). Speech, hearing, and language in de Lange syndrome. *Journal of Speech and Hearing Disorders, 35,* 66–69.

Robinson, L. K., Wolfsberg, E., & Jones, K. L. (1985). Brachmann-de Lange syndrome: Evidence for autosomal dominant inheritance. *American Journal of Medical Genetics, 22,* 109–115.

Silver, H. K. (1964). The de Lange syndrome. *American Journal of Medical Diseases of Children, 108,* 523–529.

Smith, G. F., Berg, J. M., & McCreary, B. D. (1969). de Lange syndrome. *Birth Defects: Original Article Series 5,* 18–21.

Goldenhar Syndrome

(Oculoauriculovertebral Dysplasia; First and Second Branchial Arch Syndrome; Hemifacial Microsomia)

■ Characteristics
Dysmorphology

hemifacial microsomia due to underdevelopment of the mandibular ramus and condyle

microtia with hypoplasia or atresia of external auditory canal

conductive hearing impairment

preauricular tags, most often in the line between the tragus and the corner of the mouth

lateral cleft-like extensions from the corner of the mouth, resulting in apparent macrostomia

diminished parotid gland secretions

vertebral dysplasia (hemivertebrae or hypoplasia), usually in the cervical region

Often aysmmetric and variable combinations of the following anomalies found in Goldenhar syndrome were described by Goldenhar (1952) with further delineation and review by Gorlin and Pindborg (1976):

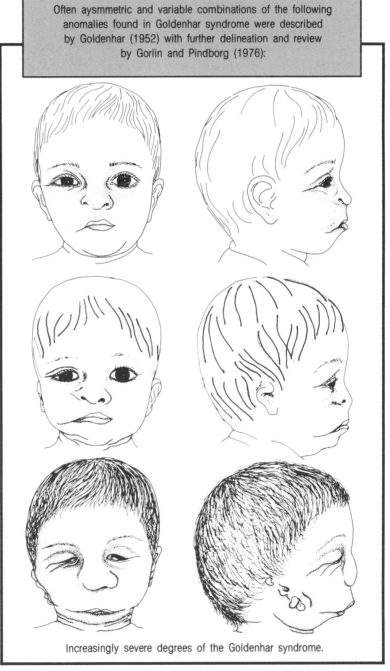

Increasingly severe degrees of the Goldenhar syndrome.

Occasional problems can include cleft lip or cleft palate, epibulbar dermoids, and congenital heart and kidney disease. Mental deficiency is reported as an infrequent finding (13 to 25 percent), and is usually mild if exhibited (Mathog & Leonard, 1980; Northern & Downs, 1974; Sparks, 1984). Milder cases may be diagnosed as hemifacial microsomia, but a careful evaluation is warranted to look for problems involving the heart or vertebral systems. The approximate incidence of this syndrome is 1 per 5,600 live births and occurs more frequently in male than in female individuals by a ratio of 3 to 2 (Grabb, 1965).

Hearing

The otological malformations associated with Goldenhar syndrome have features in common with mandibulofacial dystostosis (Treacher Collins syndrome). Malformations of the external ear commonly observed in patients with Goldenhar syndrome include preauricular tags (typically multiple), microtia, blind ended fistulas, and stenotic or atresic ear canals (Feingold & Baum, 1978; Gorlin, Jue, Jacobsen, & Goldschmidt, 1963; Summitt, 1969). Substantial variability across patients in both the degree and type of these malformations has been noted. Although middle ear anomalies are typically less severe than those associated with Treacher Collins syndrome, a variety of ossicular chain and tympanic cavity abnormalities have been documented (Bergstrom, 1980; Gorlin et al., 1963).

A detailed review of 16 patients diagnosed with Goldenhar syndrome demonstrated that, with the exception of preauricular tags, external ear anomalies were more often unilateral (Feingold & Baum, 1978). Presence of bilateral and unilateral preauricular tags was observed to occur in an approximately equal proportion for this sample of patients.

For those patients with Goldenhar syndrome who have hearing impairment, it is likely to be conductive in nature, resulting from bilateral or unilateral atresia or secondary to cleft palate, although isolated cases of sensorineural impairment have been reported (Kirkham, 1970). In the sample of 16 patients reviewed by Feingold and Baum (1978), 7 had some degree of hearing loss, with 5 having unilateral and the remaining 2 having bilateral hearing loss. The relatively high proportion of unilateral hearing impairment associated with this syndrome would seem to have important implications for otological/audiological assessment of these patients. Specifically, the presence of significant hearing impairment cannot be ruled out until detailed individual ear audiometric information has been obtained.

Speech

Oral features include high arched palate, crowding of the teeth, and occasional cleft palate or bifid uvula (Goodman & Gorlin, 1977). Mandibular involvement may range from minimal underdevelopment of the condyle to unilateral aplasia of the mandibular ramus or condyle (Gorlin & Pindborg, 1976). Incidence of clefting of the lip or palate has been reported to approach seven percent (Grabb, 1965). The facial, masticatory, and palatal muscles may be hypoplastic or dysfunctional (Luce, McGibbon, & Hoopes, 1977).

There are few published data that describe the speech and language characteristics associated with this syndrome. It is important to note that mental retardation is a rare component of Goldenhar syndrome and, as such, speech and language deficits associated with mental retardation are not expected.

Cleft palate, asymmetry of the soft palate, paresis of the soft palate, asymmetry of the tongue, and general oral structure malformations affecting unilateral movements may create resonance, articulation, and oral language production problems. Although the literature is scant (Belenchia & McCardle, 1985) concerning this syndrome, case studies suggest that language and articulation problems associated with the syndrome should be expected. In conjunction with the hearing deficit, children with Goldenhar syndrome should be considered at risk for oral language development.

Management

Genetics and Medical

Some confusion still exists relating to the specific classification of selected cases, as other first and second branchial arch syndromes have similar features to Goldenhar syndrome (Mathog & Leonard, 1980). The expressivity of the syndrome may range from mild (few apparent symptoms) to severe (complete unilateral expression of the possible facial and systemic problems). Because mental retardation is rarely severe, language and learning abilities should develop without cognitive interference.

This condition usually occurs sporadically in families. The empirical recurrence risk for first degree relatives is estimated at approximately two percent. If a parent is affected, consideration of an autosomal dominant mode of inheritance must be entertained (Summitt, 1969). This spectrum of problems is most likely heterogeneous. Discordance in monozygous twins suggests a vascular disruptive etiology in some cases (Smith, 1982).

The major differential diagnosis is with mandibulofacial dysostosis. The latter condition is usually bilateral, symmetric, and associated with a greater degree of malar hypoplasia and coloboma of the lower eyelid. Cosmetic surgery can yield favorable results.

Speech

The ultimate goals for treatment of the patient with Goldenhar syndrome fall into two categories: (1) management of structural malformations, and (2) development of appropriate speech and language skills. Treatment of structural malformations aims toward improved function and optimal facial symmetry when craniofacial growth is complete. The management procedures include increasing the size of the malformed and underdeveloped mandible, creating an articulation between the mandible and the temporal bone, and correcting malformations of the maxilla (clefts of the hard or soft palates). This management will include teamwork by plastic surgeons and orthodontists guided by developmental expectations from anthropological norms (Vargervik, Ousterhout, & Farias, 1986). Minor forms of the disorder affecting the oral cavity (clefts) will follow the guidelines for surgical correction of the palatal defects to improve speech, resonance, and voice quality.

Behavioral management revolves around the type and severity of the craniofacial expression of the syndrome. Because the child may be at risk for normal communication development based upon the hearing loss, palatal deformities, and mandibular growth, early assessment and development of a total communication program will frequently be necessary. Periodic reassessment of articulation, resonance, and voice quality, as well as evaluation of syntactic, grammatic, and pragmatic aspects of language is recommended. Special attention should be made to articulation and resonance balance following any surgical correction of the hard or soft palate region, or of the mandible (Belenchia & McCardle, 1985).

Prognosis

Early diagnosis and management of hearing or speech problems can help reduce the chance of functional impairment. The prognosis for improvement will depend upon the severity of problems and the success of the surgical, dental, or behavioral management procedures. Although the amount of data documenting changes in speech and language performance is limited, one case study (Belenchia & McCardle, 1985) noted great improvements in communication skills with a young child diagnosed at birth and treated systematically and comprehensively during the preschool years. The best results for surgical, dental, and speech and language intervention are achieved when compliance of the child and family are consistent with the goals of the team approach to management.

■ References

Belenchia, P., & McCardle, P. (1985). Goldenhar's syndrome: A case study. *Journal of Communications Disorders, 18,* 383–392.

Bergstrom, L. (1980). Assessment and consequences of malformation of the middle ear. *Birth Defects, 16,* 217–241.

Feingold, M., & Baum, J. (1976). Goldenhar's syndrome. *American Journal of Diseases of Children, 132,* 136–138.

Goldenhar, M. (1952). Associations malformatives de l'oeil et de l'oreille En particulier, le syndrome: dermoide epibulbaire-appendices auriculaires — fistula auris congenita et ses relations avec la dysostose mandibulo-faciale. *Journal de Genetique Humaine, 1,* 243–282.

Goodman, R., & Gorlin, R. (1977). *Atlas of the face in genetic disorders.* St. Louis: C. V. Mosby.

Gorlin, R., Jue, K., Jacobsen, U., & Goldschmidt, H. (1963). Oculoauriculovertebral dysplasia. *Journal of Pediatrics, 63,* 991–999.

Gorlin, R., & Pindborg, J. (1976). *Syndromes of the head and neck.* New York: McGraw-Hill.

Grabb, W. (1965). The first and second branchial arch syndrome. *Plastic and Reconstructive Surgery, 36,* 485.

Kirkham, T. (1970). Goldenhar's syndrome with inner ear defects. *Journal of Laryngology and Otology, 84,* 855–856.

Luce, E., McGibbon, B., & Hoopes, J. (1977). Velopharyngeal insufficiency in hemifacial microsomia. *Plastic and Reconstructive Surgery, 60,* 602–606.

Mathog, R., & Leonard, M. (1980). Surgical correction of Goldenhar's syndrome. *Laryngoscope, 90,* 1137–1147.

Northern, J., & Downs, M. (1974). *Hearing in children.* Baltimore: Williams & Wilkins.

Smith, D. W. (1982). *Recognizable patterns of human malformation.* Philadelphia: W. B. Saunders.

Sparks, S. (1984). *Birth defects and speech and language disorders.* San Diego: College-Hill Press.

Summitt, R. L. (1969). Familial Goldenhar syndrome. *Birth Defects, 5,* 106–109.

Vargervik, K., Ousterhout, D., & Farias, M. (1986). Factors affecting long-term results in hemifacial microsomia. *Cleft Palate Journal* (Suppl. 1), 53–68.

Moebius Syndrome
(Congenital Facial Diplegia)

■ Characteristics
Dysmorphology

facial diplegia resulting in a mask-like facies

unilateral or bilateral loss of the abductor muscles

The clinical features of Moebius syndrome are related to neurodevelopmental problems primarily affecting the 6th and 7th cranial nerves (Henderson, 1939). The signs may include (see list):

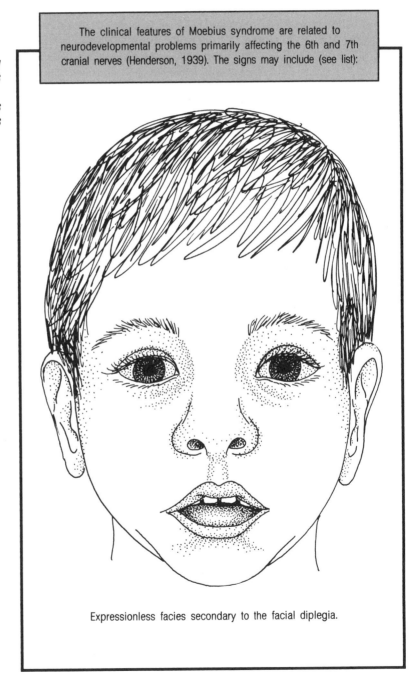

Expressionless facies secondary to the facial diplegia.

A mild degree of mental retardation is present in 10 to 15 percent of patients (Goodman & Gorlin, 1977; Gorlin, Pindborg, & Cohen, 1976; Reed & Grant, 1957). Although Meyerson and Foushee (1978) and Gorlin and colleagues (1976) have referred to the presence of hypoplastic mandibles, frequently accompanied by cleft palate (Meyerson & Foushee, 1978), these variables do not appear to be among the principal attributes of the syndrome.

Moebius syndrome may also be seen as part of a wider spectrum of facial-limb disruption. These individuals sometimes exhibit striking hypoplasia of limbs. The asymmetric and distal involvement of limbs suggests an early vascular disruption as the cause.

Hearing

Hearing impairment has been reported to occur only occasionally in individuals with Moebius syndrome. Gorlin and colleagues (1976) have reported that large, laterally protruding pinnas which may be deficient in cartilage are observed occasionally. Although the presence of sensorineural hearing impairment has been reported in isolated cases, more frequently, the impairment is conductive in nature. Of 22 patients with Moebius syndrome reviewed by Meyerson and Foushee (1978), 5 had some degree of confirmed hearing loss. Four of the patients had purely conductive hearing loss, with the remaining case demonstrating both conductive and sensorineural components. An association between abnormalities of the palate and conductive hearing impairment was noted. In addition to conductive impairment resulting from such structural abnormalities, it has been suggested that Eustachian tube dysfunction in patients with Moebius syndrome may be due to disturbed innervation of the tensor veli palatini (Kahane, 1979). Kahane has suggested that studies of Eustachian tube biomechanics are potentially helpful in describing a dysfuntion of the tensor veli palatini or Eustachian tube in patients with this syndrome.

Speech

As stated by Meyerson and Foushee (1978), involvement of the facial and hypoglossal nerves creates significant problems for speech. These include bilabial paresis (Bloomer, 1971) and lingual control problems. The lower part of the face is usually less affected than the upper portion (Reed & Grant, 1957). In support of this finding, Kahane (1979) noted that, during speech, orbicularis oris inferioris exhibits greater activity than orbicularis oris superioris. With respect to tongue involvement, these patients may be expected to show decreased ability to (1) lateralize the tongue outside the oral cavity, (2) elevate the tongue, and (3) depress or protrude the tongue (Kahane, 1979). In general, the articulators have limited strength, range, and speed of movement (Kahane, 1979; Meyerson

& Foushee, 1978). As a result, articulation competence may range from "mild distortions of phonemes requiring bilabial closure or lingual elevation to severe articulation difficulties resulting in profoundly delayed and/or unintelligible oral language" (Meyerson & Foushee, 1978, p. 361). The overall percept tends to be similar to flaccid dysarthria. Helmick (1980) likened the speech patterns of patients with Moebius syndrome to those observed in cases of bulbar palsy.

Communication development may also be adversely affected by frequent early hospital stays for aspiration problems, poor early growth due to feeding dysfunction, and reduced expectations of parents (Meyerson & Foushee, 1978). The latter variable may also be expected to contribute to receptive or expressive language delays observed in some affected children (Meyerson & Foushee, 1978).

There is little information regarding range. Meyerson and Foushee (1978) and Helmick (1980) suggested that both the extent of cranial nerve involvement and corresponding degree of motor involvement vary to a large extent. Those with more severe involvement of cranial nerves and with the most additional anomalies will encounter more severe delays and motor speech difficulties.

Management

Genetics and Medical

Moebius syndrome is undoubtedly heterogeneous in etiology. Some cases may have central nervous system factors for dysfunction, whereas others are related to myopathies. Regardless of causation, this symptom complex is equally distributed between the sexes (Kahane, 1979).

Rarely, in some families, autosomal dominant inheritance is observed (McKusick, 1986). Most commonly, the syndrome occurs sporadically. When an autosomal dominant mechanism can be ruled out, the parents' chances for another affected infant are probably low.

Facial muscle weakness may cause difficulties in feeding especially in infancy. The mask-like facies may give the impression of a developmentally delayed child, but one should not assume this to be the case. Other concerns are that the eyelids may not close completely and result in altered tearing and a predisposition to corneal and conjunctival ulceration. Artificial tears often help in preventing ulceration.

Hearing

In the event that hearing impairment is part of the constellation of difficulties, it should be treated in a manner consistent with accepted otological aural rehabilitation programs. Certainly, all patients with Moebius syndrome who have documented structural abnormalities of the palate or Eustachian tube dysfunction should be enrolled in an otological and audiological monitoring program.

Speech

Kahane (1979) suggested that speech therapy should be based on a Bobath or neuromuscular facilitation approach that stresses normalization of sensitivity and muscle tonus. The aim of such intervention would be to improve articulatory precision and swallowing abilities. Wertz (1978) discussed typical approaches to the treatment of flaccid dysarthrias. Techniques designed to improve posture, muscle strength, and articulation precision may be attempted. Helmick (1980) suggested that gains made in oral communication may be related to symptomatic management of speech behaviors. He has noted that techniques designed to improve specific muscular functioning underlying speech performance were not found to be useful. Techniques that seemed to improve performance included speech rate reduction, overarticulation, and maintenance of increased levels of vocal frequency and intensity and prosodic variability.

Meyerson and Foushee (1978) stressed early intervention on the part of the speech pathologist and audiologist in order to maximize prespeech skills and early speech and language acquisition.

Prognosis

As with any syndrome complex, prognosis will depend on degree of involvement. The number of cranial nerves involved will have a bearing on expected development. Those with central nervous system dysfunction may also be the subgroup more prone to problems of mental development. One should be careful that the mask-like facies does not lead one to erroneously believe the child is less intelligent. In terms of language, early and appropriate intervention can be expected to result in adequately intelligible speech. In more severe cases, functional oral communication will not be achievable, necessitating an alternate form of communication.

■ References

Bloomer, H. H. (1971). Speech defects associated with dental malocclusions and related abnormalities. In L. E. Travis (Ed.), *Handbook of speech pathology and audiology.* New York: Appleton-Century-Crofts.

Goodman, R., & Gorlin, R. (1977). *Atlas of the face in genetic disorders.* St. Louis: C. V. Mosby.

Gorlin, R. J., Pindborg, J. J., & Cohen, M. M. (1976). *Syndromes of the face and neck* (2nd ed., pp. 575–580). New York: McGraw-Hill.

Helmick, J. W. (1980). Speech characteristics of two children with Moebius syndrome. *Journal of Childhood Communication Disorders, 4,* 19–28.

Henderson, J. L. (1939). Congenital facial diplegia syndrome: Clinical features, pathology and aetiology; review of 61 cases. *Brain, 62,* 381.

Kahane, J. C. (1979). Pathophysiological effects of Möbius syndrome on speech and hearing. *Archives of Otolaryngology, 65,* 29–34.

McKusick, V. A. (1986). *Mendelian inheritance in man* (7th ed., pp. 494–495). Baltimore: The Johns Hopkins University Press.

Meyerson, M. D., & Foushee, D. R. (1978). Speech, language and hearing in Moebius syndrome: A study of 22 patients. *Developmental Medicine and Child Neurology, 20,* 357–365.

Reed, H., & Grant, W. (1957). Möbius's syndrome. *British Journal of Ophthalmology, 41,* 731–740.

Wertz, R. (1978). Neuropathologies of speech and language: An introduction to patient management. In D. Johns (Ed.), *Clinical management of neurogenic communication disorders.* Boston: Little, Brown and Company.

Prader-Willi Syndrome
(Prader-Labhart-Willi Syndrome)

■ Characteristics
Dysmorphology

Prader, Labhart, and Willi (1956) first delineated the characteristic features that have become associated with the distinctive Prader-Willi syndrome. Observed anomalies include (see list):

hypotonia

hypogonadism (small penis and/or cryptorchidism in male patients and labial hypoplasia in female patients)

small hands and feet

obesity

almond-shaped palpebral fissures

hypomentality

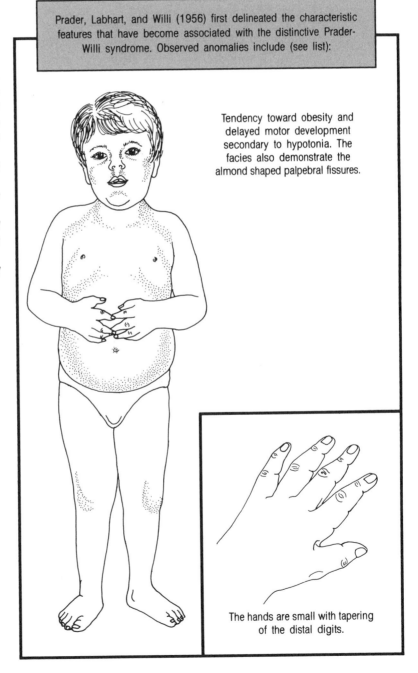

Tendency toward obesity and delayed motor development secondary to hypotonia. The facies also demonstrate the almond shaped palpebral fissures.

The hands are small with tapering of the distal digits.

These features are not easily apparent in the newborn period. Retrospectively, feeble fetal movements may have been noted. The newborn period and first year of life are characterized by feeding difficulties and low muscle tone. The genital anomalies make the diagnosis easier in male infants. Later, problems of delayed psychomotor development become more obvious. Initial failure to thrive in infancy is replaced by obesity between ages one and three. Caloric intake may not be out of proportion to that expected for height and age, but the pattern of eating is often pathological. Parents complain of constant food seeking and binge eating habits. Sometimes, making food inaccessible has included locking of cupboards and refrigerator. Behavior can also be problematic. Although individuals with Prader-Willi syndrome are usually good natured, their behavior is immature for chronological age and stubbornness and temper tantrums are frequent. The hypotonia slowly improves with time, but appetite and weight control are long-term difficulties.

There is some disagreement in the literature regarding cognitive or intellectual function in this population. Mental retardation is reported in the majority of cases, with average IQ falling between 40 and 60 (Hall & Smith, 1972; Nyhan, 1983; Ledbetter et al., 1981). Even though some affected patients score in the mentally retarded range on testing, cognitive functioning is thought to be typical for those with learning disabilities (Cassidy, 1984; Holm, 1981; Sulzbacher, Crnic, & Snow, 1981). Holm (1981) stated that over 40 percent of afflicted individuals are not mentally retarded.

Hearing

There are no reports that suggest a higher incidence of hearing loss among individuals with Prader-Willi syndrome than the incidence of hearing loss found in the general population. However, there have been reports of poorly molded and low set pinnae among individuals with Prader-Willi syndrome (Goodman & Gorlin, 1977; Gorlin, Pindborg, & Cohen, 1976). These anomalies should not have any effect on hearing ability.

Speech

The dysfunctions associated with the syndrome relate primarily to academic performance and to speech sound development. In general, children with Prader-Willi syndrome show delayed developmental landmarks. Holm (1981) reported production of single words at 21 months, sentences at 3.6 years, and development of reading ability at 7.5 years. A detailed analysis of speech and language characteristics of this population was conducted by Branson (1981). Her 21 subjects were found to be quite heterogenous in terms of linguistic abilities. Fifty-two percent demonstrated comprehension and production abilities compatible with their overall cognitive level. Three of these 11 subjects had language skills within the normal range, whereas the others were delayed 1 to 4 years below chronological age. Both Cassidy (1984) and Holm (1981) considered language to be one of the strengths of this population. The remaining 10 subjects assessed by Branson (1981) demonstrated receptive language skills far in advance of production skills. The articulation skills of this study group were substantial, a view supported by Holm (1981) and Zellweger (1969). Eighty-one percent demonstrated atypical articulation skills. Severity was variable, ranging from mild to completely unintelligible. The pattern of articulation errors was also quite variable. However, two basic patterns emerged. The first involved distortions as a result of nasal air emission. Branson was not able to determine with certainty whether these distortions were due to structural deficits, or faulty articulator placement. The second error pattern involved oral-motor difficulties. Some subjects demonstrated difficulty executing articulatory movements required for manner and place of articulation changes during connected speech.

The problems encountered by this population as a result of cognitive dysfunction are reflected in school placement data. According to Holm (1981), over 86 percent are placed in either learning disability or special education classrooms.

There are little published data concerning range in severity. Branson (1981) suggested that articulation and language ability may range from within normal limits to markedly delayed. Further, she concluded that there is not a substantial number of common elements in speech and language problems of these individuals to detail a "syndrome-specific" pattern.

Management

Genetics and Medical

There exists no consistent, widely available diagnostic marker for Prader-Willi syndrome (Cassidy, 1984). Approximately one-half of cases are associated with a small deletion in the region of the long arm of chromosome number 15 (15q11–15q13) visible by high resolution chromosome banding techniques. Because of the possible familial nature of some of these rearrangements, chromosome karyotyping should be performed in any individual suspected of having the Prader-Willi syndrome and in his or her parents. This condition usually occurs sporadically, although a few instances of familial recurrence are reported. It may be autosomal dominant with a lack of familial transmission because of the associated hypogonadism. The empiric recurrence risks are low (one to two percent).

Medical management centers around diet control and behavior management. Crnic, Sulzbacher, Snow, and Holm (1980) discussed the treatment of obesity. In their study, early intervention prevented obesity in eight children. As a group, these eight scored significantly higher on intelligence testing than untreated subjects. Often a multidisciplinary team of infant developmental specialists is required to provide the resources for patient and family support. Endocrine studies fail to show any consistent abnormalities, but patients with Prader-Willi syndrome are more prone to problems. Testosterone has also been used to treat micropenis.

Speech

Management of the development of speech and language skills in this population should necessarily involve speech and language pathologists, psychiatrists, special education professionals, and, perhaps, a nutritionist.

Sulzbacher and colleagues (1981) have highlighted management priorities at different age levels. For example, they promote adequate nutrition and stimulation for motor development in the 0 to 3 year age group. For the 3 to 6 year age group, enrollment in a preschool or early childhood education program with a behavioral or academic orientation is suggested. For school age children, special education opportunitites will undoubtedly be required. Branson (1981) suggested that there is no general treatment strategy that may be applied to the entire Prader-Willi population. Rather, individually tailored programs designed to foster receptive and expressive speech and language skills would be more beneficial.

In general, children with the Prader-Willi syndrome should receive a coordinated approach to motor, speech, and language development involving the previously mentioned professionals.

Prognosis

The life expectancy of those afflicted with Prader-Willi syndrome may be somewhat short (Zellweger, 1969). The primary cause of morbidity is cor pulmonale related to obesity (Cassidy, 1984). Prognosis for survival may be expected to improve with proper medical and nutritional management. With respect to speech and language development, all but a few may be expected to develop functional language (Holm, 1981). Timely and continued intervention by appropriate professionals may be expected to optimize speech, language, and social development.

■ References

Branson, C. (1981). Speech and language characteristics of children with Prader-Willi syndrome. In V. Holm, S. Sulzbacher, & P. Pipes (Eds.), *The Prader-Willi syndrome*. Baltimore: University Park Press.

Cassidy, S. (1984). Prader-Willi syndrome. *Current Problems in Pediatrics, 14,* 1–55.

Crnic, K., Sulzbacher, S., Snow, V., & Holm, V. (1980). Preventing mental retardation associated with gross obesity in the Prader-Willi syndrome. *Pediatrics, 66,* 787–789.

Goodman, R., & Gorlin, R. (1977). *Atlas of the face in genetic disorders.* St. Louis: C. V. Mosby.

Gorlin, R. J., Pindborg, J. J., & Cohen, M. M. (1976). *Syndromes of the head and neck* (2nd ed.). Montreal: McGraw-Hill.

Hall, B., & Smith, D. (1972). Prader-Willi syndrome. *Journal of Pediatrics, 81,* 286–293.

Holm, V. (1981). The diagnosis of Prader-Willi syndrome. In V. Holm, S. Sulzbacher, & P. Pipes (Eds.), *The Prader-Willi syndrome.* Baltimore: University Park Press.

Ledbetter, D., Riccardi, V., Airhart, S., Strobel, R., Keenan, B., & Crawford, J. (1981). Deletions of chromosome 15 as a cause of the Prader-Willi syndrome. *New England Journal of Medicine, 304,* 325–329.

Nyhan, W. (1983). Cytogenetic diseases. *Clinical Symposia, 35,* 1–32.

Prader, A., Labhart, A., & Willi, H. (1956). Ein syndrom von Adipositas, Kleinwuchs, Kryptorchismus und Oligophrenie nach myatonieartigem Zustard im Neugeborenenalter. *Schweizerische Medizinische Wochenschrift, 86,* 1260.

Sulzbacher, S., Crnic, K., & Snow, J. (1981). Behavioral and cognitive disabilities in Prader-Willi syndrome. In V. Holm, S. Sulzbacher, & P. Pipes (Eds.), *The Prader-Willi syndrome.* Baltimore: University Park Press.

Zellweger, H. (1969). The HHHO or Prader-Willi syndrome. *Birth Defects, 5,* 15–17.

Chapter 6

Environmental Syndromes

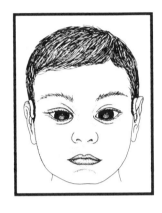

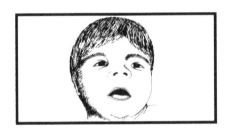

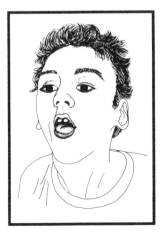

Fetal Alcohol Syndrome ■
(FAS)

Fetal Cytomegalovirus Syndrome ■
(Congenital Cytomegalic
Inclusion Disease)

Fetal Rubella Syndrome ■
(Congenital Rubella;
Gregg Syndrome)

Fetal Alcohol Syndrome (FAS)

■ Characteristics
Dysmorphology

The primary manifestations of fetal alcohol syndrome (FAS) have typically included several or all of the following characteristics (Jones & Smith, 1973); Lemoine, Harrouseau, Borteyro, & Menvet, 1968) (see list):

prenatal and postnatal growth deficiency

facial dysmorphogenesis featuring short palpebral fissures, hypoplastic philtrum, thinned upper lip, ptosis, low nasal bridge, epicanthic folds, midface hypoplasia, and posterior rotation of the ears with poorly formed concha

microcephaly with central nervous system dysfunction

mental deficiency

congenital anomalies of the heart (ventricular septal defect most common)

cervical vertebral defects

cleft palate

small teeth with faulty enamel

renal anomalies

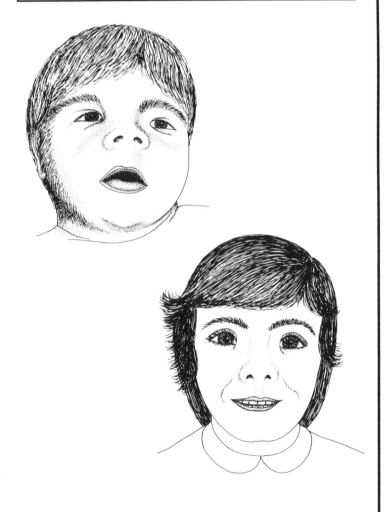

An infant and child with fetal alcohol syndrome demonstrating characteristic facial features, which include short palpebral fissures, small nose with anteverted nares, hypoplastic philtrum, thinned upper lip, and mild midfacial hypoplasia.

FAS is a distinct clinical entity exhibited among the offspring of alcoholic mothers. It occurs at a rate of about .04 percent of births, or 1 in every 2,425 term pregnancies (Sokol, 1981). In certain regions, a higher incidence has been noted, ranging from 1 in 600 in Sweden, to 1 in 1,000 in France, with the United States reporting figures of 1 in every 750 pregnancies (Little & Streissguth, 1981).

The severity of this syndrome appears to vary widely, depending upon the degree of maternal alcoholism and the timing of ingestion of the teratogen. In general, the most debilitating effects have been shown in the children of mothers reporting the heaviest and most chronic use of alcohol (Little & Streissguth, 1981). The most striking impact of the growth deficiency is in the number of cells available and in the disharmony of growth, with the eye, head, and facial region showing more problems than the general skeletal growth. The rate of growth appears to be about one-third of normal with weight gain slipping to about one-half of normal gains (Sparks, 1984).

Hearing

FAS is not characterized by any type of hearing impairment. However, dysmorphic features sometimes observed among children with FAS include protruding auricles (Smith, 1982), and posterior rotation of the ears and poorly formed concha (Clarren & Smith, 1978; Toutant & Lippmann, 1980). Those anomalies do not interfere with hearing.

Speech

Speech and language deficits have been noted in a large number of subjects. In one study, 80 percent of subjects over age one (Iosub, Fuctis, Bingel, & Gromisch, 1981) were found to have impairments of speech and language acquisition, and voice and fluency problems. Further, deficits in language appear in syntactic, semantic, and pragmatic aspects of language. Short-term memory tests also showed deficits. Many of these individuals show lower IQ scores, with the range being from average to profoundly retarded ($X = 65$) (Streissguth, Herman, & Smith, 1978). Further, IQ appears to be inversely related to severity. That is, those with the greatest degree of diagnosed aberrant deformity had correspondingly lower IQ scores (Iosub et al., 1981).

In association with general impairment in mental functioning, language learning disabilities and hyperactivity consistent with minimal brain dysfunction have been noted (Lippman, 1980; Shaywitz, Cohen, & Shaywitz, 1980). The hyperactivity is characterized by impulsivity, cognitive and perceptual deficits, and multiple problems in academic and social performance (Bellak, 1977; Sparks, 1984).

Recently, Becker, Leeper, and Warr-Leeper (1985) and Becker, Warr-Leeper, and Leeper (1985) compared communication skills of children with FAS and matched control subjects. All but one of the children with FAS demonstrated abnormalities of the oral-peripheral speech mechanism. Mental age inconsistent articulation abilities were present in approximately half of the subjects. Mental age inconsistent abilities in the comprehension and use of grammatical markers was also demonstrated. The children with FAS also showed reduced ability to process and store critical elements when assessed by memory tasks. Resonance problems consisting of hypernasality and nasal air emission of air and weak or omitted consonants may be present if a cleft of the palate is part of the deficit.

Although the effects may be related to the amount of alcohol consumed and the chronicity of the problems, speech and language problems may be both mental age (i.e., IQ) consistent or inconsistent, depending upon the linguistic parameters measured. The more severe the effects passed on to the child, the more opportunity for physical, as well as cognitive and linguistic, impairment.

Management

Genetics and Medical

The question often arises as to the definition of a dangerous level of alcohol consumption during pregnancy. Although most risk data are based upon the chronic use of alcohol in pregnancy, there have been reports of FAS associated with binge drinking. In addition to amount and frequency of alcohol ingestion, the presence or absence of fetal effects can be influenced by the timing of the exposure (i.e., periods of extreme fetal susceptibility) and genetic enzymatic variation (polymorphisms) responsible for the metabolic breakdown of alcohol and its metabolites.

Embryos exposed to one or two ounces of absolute alcohol per day, on the average, may show growth deficiency, lowered intelligence, and facial changes, but full effects of FAS may be seen in neonates who have been exposed to more than two ounces of alcohol per day on average.

Speech

For children identified as having FAS, development of speech and language is at risk. As noted, severity and subtypes of linguistic involvement relate to the peripheral and/or central nervous system damage. Early language and speech assessment will be necessary. Additionally, cognitive testing should provide information about whether general or specific learning deficits exist. Based upon functioning level, early speech and language intervention should be expected. Specific deficits in short-term memory and concentration may interfere with general language therapy procedures and may demand more individual therapy in a restricted, less active environment. Sparks (1984) has noted that little data are available about the effects of intervention on later speech and language skills. In several instances, however, there was a lack of "catch-up" in children studied who had FAS. Thus, IQ consistent language behavior should be expected with those children moderately to severely affected by fetal alcohol exposure.

Articulation problems may relate to developmental errors or to velopharyngeal incompetence secondary to a cleft of the hard or soft palate. Children with palatal clefts will require surgery and/or prosthetic management during the first year to 18 months of life to attain adequate velopharyngeal closure and hence, more normal resonance balance and articulation development. Traditional management techniques are usually employed for "functional" articulation disorders. Treatment of language learning disabilities, including reading, writing, and mathematical skills, should be noted by school special education personnel. Special language learning classes or resource classroom schedules for those with lower cognitive skills may be employed. Periodic reassessment of language and language development should occur as the child gets older.

Prognosis

Prognosis for improvement will be dependent upon the severity of the disorder and the type of cognitive, linguistic, and/or psychosocial involvement. If cognitive deficits are present, language and speech will follow mental age consistent behavior and be necessarily slow. Minimal problems related to more scattered and less chronic effects may respond well to behavioral therapy techniques. Little data relating to gains in speech and language performance are available, but Sparks (1984) has noted that there is a limited ability for many of these children to catch up mentally or physically, as compared to those children who have been malnourished prenatally. Thus, early identification of specific deficits, therapy geared to disorders, and consistent reassessment as the child matures may be expected to provide more information concerning gains in communication skills.

■ References

Becker, M., Warr-Leeper, G. A., & Leeper, H. A. (1985, May). *Fetal alcohol syndrome: A description of short-term memory, grammatical, and semantic abilities.* Paper presented at the Canadian Speech and Hearing Association Convention, Toronto.

Becker, M., Leeper, H. A., & Warr-Leeper, G. A. (1985, May). *Fetal alcohol syndrome: A description of oral motor and articulation characteristics.*

Paper presented at the Candian Speech and Hearing Association Convention, Toronto.

Bellak, L. (1977). Psychiatric states in adults with minimal brain dysfunction. *Psychiatric Annals, 7,* 575–589.

Clarren, S., & Smith, D. W. (1978). The fetal alcohol syndrome. *The New England Journal of Medicine, 298,* 1063–1067.

Iosub, S., Fuctis, M., Bingel, N., & Gromisch, D. (1981). Fetal alcohol syndrome revisited. *Pediatrics, 68,* 4175–4179.

Jones, K. L., & Smith, D. W. (1973). Recognition of the fetal alcohol syndrome in early infancy. *Lancet, 2,* 999–1001.

Lemoine, P., Harrousseau, H., Borteyro, J. P., & Menvet, J. C. (1968). Les enfants de parents alcoholoques: anomalies observees, a propos de 127 cas. *Archives Francaise de Pediatrie, 25,* 830–832.

Lippman, S. (1980). Prenatal alcohol and minimum brain dysfunction. *Southern Medical Journal, 73,* 1173–1174.

Little, R. E., & Streissguth, A. P. (1981). Effects of alcohol on the fetus: Impact and prevention. *Canadian Medical Association Journal, 125,* 159–164.

Shaywitz, S., Cohen, D., & Shaywitz, B. (1980). Behavior and learning difficulties in children of normal intelligence to alcoholic mothers. *Journal of Pediatrics, 96,* 978–982.

Smith, D. W. (1982). *Recognizable patterns of human malformations* (3rd ed.). Philadelphia: W. B. Saunders.

Sokol, R. J. (1981). Alcohol and abnormal outcomes of pregnancy. *Canadian Medical Association Journal, 125,* 143–148.

Sparks, S. N. (1984, February). Speech and language in fetal alcohol syndrome. *ASHA,* 27–31.

Streissguth, A. P., Herman, C. S., & Smith, D. W. (1978). Intelligence behaviour and dysmorphogenesis in the fetal alcohol syndrome: A report on 20 patients. *Journal of Pediatrics, 92*(3), 363–367.

Toutant, C., & Lippmann, S. (1980). Fetal alcohol syndrome. *American Family Physician, 22,* 113–117.

Fetal Cytomegalovirus Syndrome
(Congenital Cytomegalic Inclusion Disease)

■ Characteristics
Dysmorphology

microcephaly/mental retardation

periventricular calcifications

obstructive hydrocephalus

optic atrophy/chorioretinitis

hearing impairment

Cytomegalovirus (CMV) is a member of the herpes virus group frequently responsible for maternal and fetal infection. It is estimated that one percent of all newborns are infected with CMV, but that the majority of primary CMV infections are asymptomatic (Knox, 1983; Kumar et al., 1984). CMV infection may be rarely associated with severe neurological sequelae which can include (see list):.

Microcephaly with psychomotor retardation.

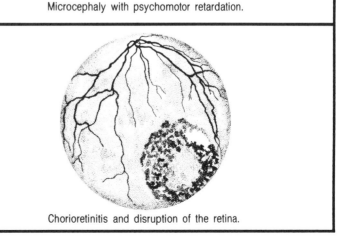

Chorioretinitis and disruption of the retina.

259

There exists some controversy regarding relative risks. Some have suggested that fetal CMV infection should not be a criteria for pregnancy termination and that screening for primary CMV infection in pregnancy is of limited value (Preece et al., 1983). Other studies have documented possible increased risks of neurological damage, but there is probably an element of bias of ascertainment in their study populations (Alford et al., 1977; Hanshaw, 1971; Hanshaw, Scheiner, & Moxley, 1976; Kumar, Nankervis, & Gold, 1973; Reynolds et al., 1974).

Hearing

In areas where effective rubella prevention programs have been established, cytomegalic inclusion disease is possibly the most common cause of nonhereditary congenital hearing impairment. The prevalence of significant sensorineural hearing impairment resulting from CMV is unknown, due to the relatively large number of asymptomatic births, the wide range of associated hearing loss, and the potential for delayed onset of auditory related problems. Current estimates range from approximately 15 percent in children with subclinical CMV (Stagno, 1977) to nearly 30 percent in symptomatic cases (Pass & Stagno, 1980). In a large-scale prospective study (Harris, Ahlfors, Ivarsson, Lernmark, & Svanberg, 1984), 50 out of 10,328 infants were identified as having CMV infections at birth. Of these, 43 were followed over a 5 year period. Five (12 percent) of the children had hearing impairment, with four of the five demonstrating profound bilateral hearing loss and transient signs of imbalance.

The otoneurological complications resulting from cytomegalic inclusion disease may include extensive invasion of the cochlea and semicircular canals as well as structures of the central auditory nervous system, including the cochlear nuclei, brainstem nuclei, and cerebral cortex. Postmortem histopathological studies of two infants identified cytomegalic inclusions in the epithelial cells lining the stria vascularis, Reissner's membrane, and the semicircular canals (Davis, 1969; Meyers & Stool, 1968). Interestingly, in both reports, a notable sparing of the structures of the organ of Corti and spiral ganglion was observed. Unfortunately, the auditory status of these two infants was unknown.

According to Northern and Downs (1984), there is no characteristic pattern of sensorineural hearing impairment associated with CMV. Studies have documented hearing loss resulting from CMV to range from very mild to profound which may be either bilateral or unilateral in nature. It is important to note that progressive sensorineural hearing impairment has been documented in children having congenital CMV (Dahle, McCollister, & Hamner, 1974). This would appear to be related to the fact that active infection may persist into the eighth year of life (Hanshaw, 1971).

Speech

The occurrence of hearing deficits may be expected (depending on their severity) to affect language development. In a similar vein, the presence of intellectual handicaps may be associated with developmental delay, poor gross motor control, learning disabilities, and school performance problems.

The data summarized by Alford and colleagues (1977) suggest that neurological deficits may range from mild to severe. Kumar and colleagues (1984) suggested the same in the case of auditory impairments. Comments regarding range of involvement in CMV are difficult to interpret given the different methods of detection and their inherent association with different degrees of involvement.

Management

Genetics and Medical

Owing to the widespread occurrence of CMV in the general population, little can be done to prevent primary infection in pregnancy.

Hearing

Although controversial, a possible plan for early auditory management is the screening of newborns for congenital CMV infection. Harris and colleagues (1984) have questioned the effectiveness of prenatal serological tests and, rather, advocate the use of CMV isolations performed within one to two weeks after birth. In view of the potentially long-term degenerative nature of the disease, thorough audiological assessments performed at relatively short intervals of between three to six months are recommended during preschool years. For such a program to be successful, the parents must be helped to understand the importance of long-term audiological monitoring.

Speech

Because speech and language development may be compromised by the presence of a hearing impairment or intellectual involvement, speech and language therapy may be beneficial for certain children.

Prognosis

Prognosis will vary depending on severity of involvement. In cases of hearing or intellectual impairment, early intervention and close follow-up will optimize speech and language development.

■ References

Alford, C., Stagno, S., Reynolds, D., Dahle, A., Amos, C., & Saxon, S. (1977). Long-term mental and perceptual defects associated with silent intrauterine infections. In L. Gluck (Ed.), *Intrauterine asphyxia and the developing fetal brain* (pp. 377–393). Chicago: Year Book Medical.

Dahle, A., McCollister, F., & Hamner, B. (1974). Subclinical congenital cytomegalovirus infection and hearing impairment. *Journal of Speech and Hearing Disorders, 39,* 320–329.

Davis, G. (1969). Cytomegalovirus in the inner ear. *Annals of Otology, Rhinology and Laryngology, 78,* 1179–1187.

Hanshaw, J. (1971). Congenital cytomegalovirus infection: A fifteen year perspective. *Journal of Infectious Diseases, 123,* 555–561.

Hanshaw, J., Scheiner, A., & Moxley, A. (1976). School failure and deafness after "silent" congenital cytomegalovirus infection. *New England Journal of Medicine, 296,* 468.

Harris, S., Ahlfors, K., Ivarsson, S., Lernmark, B., & Svanberg, L. (1984). Congenital cytomegalovirus infection and sensorineural hearing loss. *Ear and Hearing, 5,* 352–355.

Knox, G. E. (1983). Cytomegalovirus: Patient counseling. *Seminars in Perinatology, 7*(1), 43–46.

Kumar, M., Nankervis, G., & Gold, E. (1973). Inapparent congenital cytomegalovirus infection: A follow-up study. *New England Journal of Medicine, 288,* 1370.

Kumar, M., Nankervis, G., Jacobs, I., Ernhart, C., Glasson, C., McMillan, P., & Gold, E. (1984). Congenital and postnatally acquired cytomegalovirus infections: Long-term follow-up. *Journal of Pediatrics, 104,* 674–679.

Meyers, E., & Stool, S. (1968). Cytomegalic inclusion disease of the inner ear. *Laryngoscope, 78,* 1904–1914.

Northern, J., & Downs, M. (1984). *Hearing in children* (3rd ed., pp. 243–244). Baltimore: Williams & Wilkins.

Pass, R., & Stagno, S. (1980). Outcome of symptomatic congenital cytomegalovirus infection: Results of long-term longitudinal follow-up. *Pediatrics, 66,* 758–762.

Preece, P. M., Blount, J. M., Glover, J., Fletcher, G. M., Peckham, C. S., & Griffiths, P. D. (1983). The consequences of primary cytomegalovirus infection in pregnancy. *Archives of Disease in Children, 58,* 970–975.

Reynolds, D., Stagno, S., Stubbs, K., Dahle, A., Livingston, M., Saxon, S., & Alford, C. (1974). Inapparent congenital cytomegalovirus infection with elevated cord IgM levels: Causal relations with auditory and mental deficiency. *New England Journal of Medicine, 290,* 291.

Stagno, S. (1977). Auditory and visual defects resulting from symptomatic and sub-clinical congenital CMV and toxoplasma infections. *Pediatrics, 59,* 669–687.

Fetal Rubella Syndrome
(Congenital Rubella; Gregg Syndrome)

■ Characteristics
Dysmorphology

Fetal rubella was one of the first well documented examples (Gregg, 1941) of a harmful environmental agent causing fetal malformation. This RNA virus may cause mild or asymptomatic disease in adults but have devastating effects on fetal development. In addition to transient signs or symptoms associated with congenital infections, permanent fetal damage may cause one or more of the following disorders (see list):

hearing impairment (sensorineural deafness, either unilateral or bilateral)

cataract, glaucoma, or chorioretinitis

congenital heart disease (usually septal defects), patent ductus arteriosus

central nervous system disorders (microcephaly, mental deficiency)

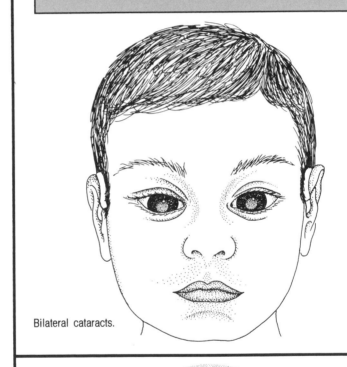

Bilateral cataracts.

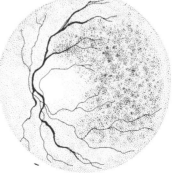

"Salt and pepper" retinopathy.

The degree and probability of organ damage depends on the timing of the infection during gestation. Prospective data (Sallomi, 1966) suggest that fetal infection in the first month of pregnancy carries a very high risk of significant fetal abnormality (60 percent). In the second and third months of gestation, this risk is reduced to approximately 25 percent and 8 percent, respectively. Risks in the second trimester are small, and negligible in the third trimester.

A number of long-term follow-up studies of children affected during the 1964–65 rubella epidemic have provided comprehensive prevalence and longitudinal data. In the preschool population, cardiac (33 percent), neurologic (33 percent), visual (33 percent), and hearing (47 to 73 percent) deficits are reported (Chess, Fernandez, & Korn, 1978; Desmond et al., 1985; Menser & Reye, 1974). Chess and colleagues reported the existence of mental retardation in 37 percent of their study population. A value of 42 percent was cited by Vernon and Hicks (1980). Impulsivity is reportedly more common in those afflicted with this syndrome (Chess & Fernandez, 1980; Hicks, 1970; Vernon, 1969). Learning disabilities also tend to be associated with this syndrome (Feldman, Lajoie, Mendelson, & Pinsky, 1971; Jensema, 1974; Lehman & Simmons, 1972; Vernon, 1967, 1969). Chess and colleagues (1978) reported the incidence of autism to be 7.4 percent, compared to an expected incidence of 0.7 per 10,000. Desmond and colleagues (1985) referred to the prevalence of cerebral dysfunction affecting motor coordination, balance, and learning ability.

In patients evaluated at ages 16 to 18 years, many of the conditions reported in the preschool years remain, although not necessarily to the same degree. For example, the incidence of mental retardation dropped from 37 percent to 26 percent (Chess et al., 1978). Conversely, some children originally diagnosed as nondisabled were later found by Vernon and Hicks (1980) to be autistic or mentally retarded. Although Desmond and colleagues (1985) reported a 47 percent incidence of hearing loss in the birth to 18 month age group, 92 percent of those evaluated at age 16 to 18 were diagnosed with hearing loss.

The incidence of the syndrome in general has obviously dropped dramatically since the development of a vaccine. However, patients do continue to appear in pediatric practices (Desmond et al., 1985).

Hearing

Sensorineural hearing impairment is one of the most frequently observed features associated with this disease (Borton & Stark, 1970; Pumper & Yamashiroya, 1975). According to Northern and Downs (1984), the most frequent delayed manifestation of congenital rubella syndrome is progressive sensorineural hearing impairment. It has been estimated that some degree of progression may be observed in up to 25 percent of children with fetal rubella syndrome (Bordley & Alford, 1970).

General agreement can be found in the literature concerning the temporal bone characteristics associated with congenital rubella syndrome. A review of common temporal bone findings has been provided by Brookhouser and Bordley (1973) and includes a sacculocochlear change of the Scheibe type with partial collapse of the Reissner membrane and adherence of the membrane to the stria vascularis and organ of Corti, atrophy and/or some destruction of the elements of the stria vascularis, and a rolling up of the tectorial membrane being most pronounced within the basal end of the cochlea. The literature on congenital rubella syndrome suggests the possibility of some form of middle ear abnormality in addition to the more commonly observed and more extensively documented sensorineural impairment. Richards (1964), for example, reported stapedial footplate fixation in three children with congenital rubella syndrome.

Although variability does exist with regard to the resulting type, degree, and configuration of hearing loss, the majority of children with hearing impairment secondary to maternal rubella exhibit bilateral sensorineural hearing loss of a moderately severe to profound degree. Additionally, the majority of children demonstrate hearing loss that is relatively symmetrical bilaterally. With regard to audiometric configuration, several characteristic forms have been observed, with the three most common including relatively flat, trough-shaped, or gradually falling. In a recent review of audiograms collected from 32 children with fetal rubella syndrome, Anvar, Mencher, and Keet (1984) demonstrated that nearly 72 percent of the individual ear audiograms could be described as either "essentially flat" or "gradually sloping" (see Figure 6-1a, b). Additionally, 75 percent of these children had symmetrical contours bilaterally. One interesting finding of this retrospective study, having obvious implications for management, was that 92 percent of the children developed middle ear pathology sufficient to require at least one myringotomy with placement of ventilation tubes.

Speech

The sensorineural hearing loss, if present, may be expected to adversely affect the development of speech and language as may any associated behavioral and intellectual disorders. School performance may be less than optimal in some cases as a result of impulsivity, poor motor coordination, intellectual deficits, attentional disorders, or associated learning disabilities.

Management

Genetics and Medical

Primary prevention is possible through sucessful immunization of all children. Nonimmune women of child-bearing age should be

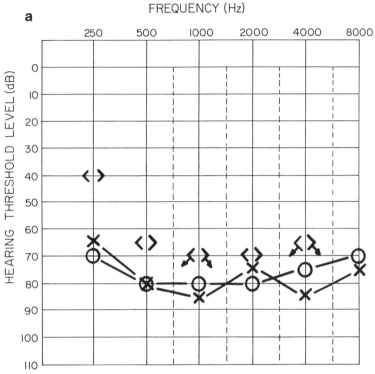

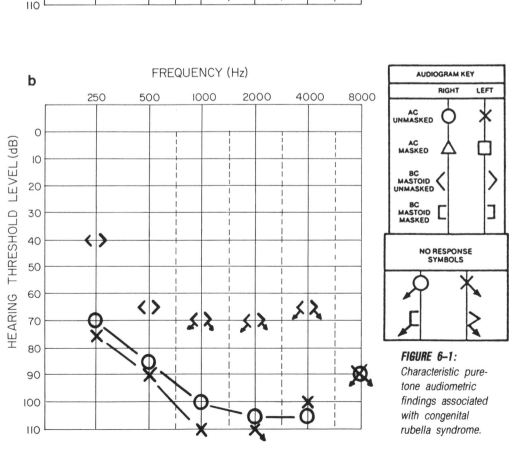

FIGURE 6-1:
Characteristic pure-tone audiometric findings associated with congenital rubella syndrome.

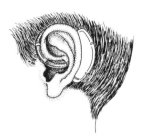

FIGURE 6–2:
*Unilateral or bilateral
hearing impairment.*

immunized before a pregnancy occurs, but there are instances of rubella vaccination in pregnant women. Available data would indicate that the risk for fetal malformation from vaccination is extremely low or nonexistent (Modlin, Brandling-Bennett, Witte, Campbell, & Meyer, 1975). However, the recommendation to avoid pregnancy for 3 months after immunization should still be made.

Hearing

As for cytomegalovirus infections, the possibility of progressive hearing impairment has important implications for audiological management. In addition to all other management strategies relevant to sensorineural hearing impairment in early childhood, the frequent and careful monitoring of hearing sensitivity and hearing aid output characteristics is essential with the child who has rubella syndrome (see Figure 6–2). Northern and Downs (1984) have recommended that children with a suspected history of rubella should be followed audiologically until 18 to 24 months of age.

Speech

As is the case with all conditions involving hearing impairment, speech and language therapy may be required to facilitate development. The prevalence of intellectual and behavioral handicaps will undoubtedly dictate the involvement of special education personnel in the education and vocational training of these children.

Prognosis

Prognosis necessarily varies with the degree of severity of the syndrome. Some aspects of the syndrome (i.e., cognitive and behavioral conditions) may be expected to improve without direct treatment as a result of the body's immune system overcoming the chronic viral infection, allowing for a reorganization of brain function (Chess et al., 1978). Early initiation and continuation of regular medical and intellectual monitoring and appropriate involvement of audiology, speech and language, and special education personnel are necessary to optimize the development of these patients.

■ References

Anvar, B., Mencher, G., & Keet, S. (1984). Hearing loss and congenital rubella in Atlantic Canada. *Ear and Hearing, 5,* 340–348.

Bordley, J., & Alford, B. (1970). The pathology of rubella deafness. *International Audiology, 9,* 58–67.

Borton, T., & Stark, E. (1970). Audiological findings in hearing loss secondary to maternal rubella. *Pediatrics, 45,* 225–229.

Brookhouser, P., & Bordley, J. (1973). Congenital rubella deafness: Pathology and pathogenesis. *Archives of Otolaryngology, 98,* 252–257.

Chess, S., & Fernandez, P. (1980). Neurologic damage and behavior disorder in rubella children. *American Annals of the Deaf, 125,* 998–1001.

Chess, S., Fernandez, P., & Korn, S. (1978). Behavioral consequences of congenital rubella. *Journal of Pediatrics, 98,* 699–703.

Desmond, M., Wilson, G., Vorderman, A., Murphy, M., Thurber, S., Fisher, E., & Kroulik, E. (1985). The health and educational status of adolescents with congenital rubella syndrome. *Developmental Medicine and Child Neurology, 27,* 721–729.

Feldman, R., Lajoie, R. Mendelson, J., & Pinsky, L. (1971). Congenital rubella and language disorders, *Lancet, 2,* 978.

Gregg, N. (1941). Congenital cataracts following German measles in the mother. *Transactions of Ophthalmological Societies of Australia, 3,* 35.

Hicks, D. (1970). Comparison of profiles of rubella and non-rubella children. *American Annals of the Deaf, 115,* 86–92.

Jensema, C. (1974). Post-rubella children in special education programs for the hearing impaired. *Volta Review, 76,* 466–473.

Lehman, J., & Simmons, M. (1972). Comparison of rubella and non-rubella young deaf adults: Implications for learning. *Journal of Speech and Hearing Research, 15,* 734–742.

Menser, M., & Reye, R. (1974). The pathology of congenital rubella: A review written by request. *Pathology, 6,* 215–218.

Modlin, J. F., & Brandling-Bennett, D., Witte, J. J., Campbell, C. C., & Meyers, J. D. (1975). A review of five years experience with rubella vaccine in the United States. *Pediatrics, 55,* 20–29.

Northern, J., & Downs, M. (1984). *Hearing in children* (3rd ed., p. 243). Baltimore: Williams & Wilkins.

Pumper, R., & Yamashiroya, H. (1975). Essentials of medical virology. Philadelphia: W. B. Saunders.

Richards, C. (1964). Middle ear changes in rubella deafness. *Archives of Otolaryngology, 80,* 48–53.

Sallomi, S. J. (1966). Rubella in pregnancy: A review of prospective studies from the literature. *Obstetrics and Gynecology, 27,* 252–256.

Vernon, M. (1967). Characteristics associated with post rubella deaf children. *Volta Review, 69,* 176–185.

Vernon, M. (1969). Multiple handicapped deaf children: Medical, educational, and psychological considerations. *Council of Exceptional Children, Research Monograph, 18,* 1.

Vernon, M., & Hicks, D. (1980). Overview of rubella, herpes simplex, cytomegalovirus, and other viral diseases: Their relationship to deafness. *American Annals of the Deaf, 125,* 529–534.

Glossary
of Genetic and Medical Terms

abducens palsy — a paralysis of the sixth cranial nerve.

acentric chromosome — a chromosome that possesses no centromere for spindle fiber attachment.

achondroplasia — one of the more common forms of dwarfism.

acrocentric chromosome — a chromosome in which the centromere (or spindle fiber attachment point) is close to one end of the chromosome.

allele — a gene situated at a particular locus on a particular chromosome may exist in more than one form; the different forms of a particular gene are called alleles of that gene. Different alleles of the same gene produce different effects during development.

Alzheimer's disease — presenile dementia usually associated with sclerosis or neurofibral degeneration.

amenorrhea — lack of menstrual periods.

amniocentesis — needle puncture of the uterus and amniotic cavity to allow amniotic fluid to be withdrawn by syringe. The term is often (loosely) applied to the whole procedure of prenatal diagnosis by culture and analysis of amniotic fluid cells or amniotic fluid.

anencephaly — a form of spina bifida in which the brain fails to develop.

aneuploidy — the occurrence of a chromosome number different from the usual number and not an exact multiple of the haploid number. An individual subject may be aneuploid, as in Down syndrome, or occasional cells within an otherwise diploid individual may be aneuploid.

ankylosis — stiffening of a joint.

anosmia — the inability to smell.

arthropathy — a disease involving joints.

association — the occurrence of two or more genetic traits together in the same individual. Association may be due to two linked genes, multiple (pleiotropic) effects of the same gene, or to the random association of two nonlinked genes in the same individual.

ataxia — loss of coordinated muscle movements.

atresia — severe underdevelopment of an opening or passage resulting in pathologic closure.

autosomal linkage — the linkage of two genes on an autosome.

autosome — any chromosome other than a sex chromosome.

banding — the techniques of staining chromosomes in a characteristic pattern of cross bands, thus allowing individual identication of each chromosome pair. Giemsa banding (G banding) and quinacrine fluorescence banding (Q banding) are the best known banding techniques.

brachycephaly — shortness of the anterior to posterior diameter of the skull.

brachydactyly — shortness of the fingers.

Brushfield spots — the hypopigmented spots that can be seen in the irides of certain individuals with Down syndrome.

BSER (Brainstem Evoked Response Audiometry) — averaging responses produced by the auditory nerve and the brainstem following the onset of tone bursts. This procedure may be used to measure hearing activity.

canthus — the corner of the eye slit.

carriers — individuals carrying a gene and capable of passing it on, but who do not themselves show the full effects of the gene because: (1) the individual may be a heterozygote for a recessive gene or for a gene that produces only slight effects in single dose; (2) the gene may be a late acting one, the subject being examined before the gene has expressed itself; and (3) the effects of the gene may be masked by other genes called modifier genes, or by environmental modifiers.

centromere — the constricted region of a chromosome where spindle fibers attach during cell division.

cholesteatoma — a mass (i.e., tumor) of skin-like tissue which invades the middle ear and the mastoid spaces. The growth of the tumor may be caused by a perforation of the tympanic membrane or chronic otitis media.

chorion frondosum — the part of the fetal membranes that develops into the fetal part of the placenta.

chorionic villus sampling — a relatively new prenatal diagnostic technique which involves obtaining tissue from the developing area of the placenta known as the chorion.

chorioretinitis — inflammation of the choroid membrane and retinal structure of the eye.

chromosomes — structural elements of various sizes found in the nucleus of a cell and containing the major part of the hereditary material (the genes). The main chemical components of a chromosome are proteins and DNA. They are capable of self-duplication, thus ensuring that identical genetic material is handed to each of the daughter cells resulting from a cell division.

clinodactyly — abnormal incurving of the fingers.

coarctation of the aorta — a narrowing of the aorta, the major artery leading from the heart.

coloboma — a clefting defect of the eye which may involve iris, choroid, or retinal structures.

condyle — the rounded articular surface of a bone.

congenital — present at birth. No necessary connotation as to genetic or nongenetic causation (e.g., the rubella syndrome is congenital but nongenetic).

consanguineous union — union between biologically related individuals, that is, individuals having one or more ancestors in common. Various degrees of consanguinity are recognized.

craniosynostosis — premature fusion of the cranial sutures.

cryptorchidism — undescended testes.

cubitus valgus — observed bending of the extended lower arm to the outside of the upper limb axis due to a difference in elbow joint anatomy.

cutis marmorata — a marbled appearance of the skin usually due to an abnormality in vascular structure.

cytogenetics — a branch of genetics dealing with the cytological basis of heredity, that is, with the study of the chromosomes, particularly during the cell division and the relationship of chromosome variation to the genotype and phenotype of the individual.

cytomegalic inclusion disease — significant problems that are the result of cytomegalovirus infection in utero. Characteristically, inclusion bodies can be demonstrated within certain cells after the infection.

deletion — the loss of a segment of a chromosome.

dentinogenesis imperfecta — opalescent dentin due to a hereditary defect of dentin formation.

diploid — possessing a double set of chromosomes, one set of which was derived from the mother and one set from the father (synonym: *2n*).

dizygotic twins (dizygous or DZ twins) — twins resulting from the fertilization of two ova by two spermatozoa (synonym: *fraternal twins*).

DNA (deoxyribose nucleic acid) — the main chemical component of the genetic material in chromosomes. The Watson–Crick theroy of DNA structure provides a basis for understanding both how chromosomes replicate themselves and how genetic "information" is stored in the genetic material. The DNA molecules are composed of nucleotides in the form of a chain. Each nucleotide contains an organic base (adenine, guanine, thymine, cytosine), a sugar (deoxyribose), and phosphate. The specific nature of the genes is based on the specific sequence of base pairs in the molecule.

dominant gene — a gene that expresses its effect even when it is present only in single doses, that is, in the presence of a different (recessive) allele. Dominance may be *complete* when the full effect of a gene is produced in single dose, or *incomplete* (partial) when the gene produces an easily detectable effect in a single dose, but a more marked effect in a double dose.

duplication — the occurrence of a chromosomal segment in duplicate, resulting from chromosome breakage and reunion of noncorresponding ends (unequal crossing-over).

dysmorphic — abnormality of form or shape.

dysplasia — abnormal development of tissue.

ectodermal — those parts of the body derived from the outer layer of cells in an embryo (e.g., skin, hair).

ectrodactyly — congenital absence of one or more digits of the hands or feet.

empirical risk — the prediction of the probability that a genetic or congenital abnormality will recur in a family in which it has already occurred. The empirical risk figures are based upon the study of the reproductive history of couples who have borne a child who is malformed or otherwise disabled.

epicanthal folds — the folds of skin sometimes seen on the inner aspect of the palpebral fissure and that ovelap the inner canthus. Commonly seen in the Asian population and as a feature of certain syndromes such as Down syndrome.

epitympanum — the portion of the tympanic cavity (middle ear cavity) extending beyond the superior border of the tympanic membrane.

exophthalmos — abnormal protrusion of the eyeballs.

exostosis — a bony tumor/protuberance on the surface of a bone.

expressivity — the degree of severity of expression of a gene in a particular individual. Some genes are of variable expressivity, such as that for the symptom triad of blue sclerae, brittle bones, and deafness; some of those processing this gene show all three effects, whereas others may show only two, or even one, of the three possible effects of the gene.

familial — the situation where several individuals in a family group are affected, not necessarily the result of a genetic mechanism.

fertilization — fusion between the male gamete (spermatozoon) and the female gamete (ovum). The essence of fertilization lies in the combination of a haploid set of maternal chromosomes with a haploid set of paternal chromosomes.

fibroblast — a connective tissue cell such as skin.

fistula — a sinus or passage leading from one organ surface to another.

frontal bossing — prominence of the forehead.

fungiform papillae — minute elevations on the tongue.

gamete — a mature male or female reproductive cell; spermatozoon or ovum; normally, with a haploid set of chromosomes.

gametogenesis — the process of formation of sperm and eggs.

gene — a unit situated at a particular locus on a chromosome, concerned with the determination of a specific protein or protein-like material.

genetic counseling — guidance to individuals about the possibility of occurrence or recurrence (in instances where a known condition has already occurred) of specific genetically determined defects in themselves or close relatives, especially future children.

genetic heterogeneity — a certain phenotype can be produced by two or more different genetic mechanisms.

genetic marker — a readily "recognizable" gene or chromosome which can be used in family and population studies to mark the route of transmission or frequency of that particular gene or chromosome.

genome — a complement or complete set of genes, characteristic of a species or an individual.

genotype — the genetic makeup of an individual; this may refer to one locus or several loci.

glomerulus — the capillary tufts associated with the nephron of the kidney.

glossoptosis — downward displacement of the tongue.

gonadal — relating to the gonads (testis or ovary).

hallux — the large toe.

haploid — possessing a single set of chromosomes, as in the reproductive cells (synonym: *In*).

hemizygous — a state in which only the allele of a particular genic locus is present in a nucleus such as a sex chromosome *in a male*. Thus, the gene may be on part of the X which has no homologue on the Y. In either case, the gene will have no allele and will, therefore, express its effect, even if it is a recessive allele.

heterochromia irides — different colors of the iris.

heterozygote — one who possesses two different alleles of a gene at a particular locus on a pair of homologous chromosomes.

heterozygous — possessing two different alleles of a particular gene on a pair of homologous chromosomes.

hirsutism — excessive facial or body hair.

homologous chromosomes — all the chromosomes of a diploid set (except the sex chromosomes in a male) can be paired off into corresponding or homologous pairs. In humans there are 22 pairs of homologous autosomes, plus the sex chromosome pair.

homozygote — one who possesses identical alleles of a gene at a particular locus on two homologous chromosomes.

homozygous — possessing identical alleles of a particular gene on a pair of homologous chromosomes.

hydantoin — drug used in the treatment of epilepsy; commonly referred to by it trade name, Dilantin.

hypercholesterolemia — increased levels of cholesterol in blood.

hyperplasia — increase in the size or bulk of a body tissue as a result of an increase in cell number.

hypertelorism — increased distance between the eyes.

hypertrophy — overgrowth of a tissue or body organ usually due to an increase in cell size, but not in number.

hypodontia — less than the expected number of teeth.

hypogonadism — decreased gonadal function usually manifesting as deficient gonadal hormone production.

hypoplasia — incomplete or underdevelopment of a tissue or organ.

hypospadias — a defect of the wall of the urethra, such that the urethral opening is on the underside of the penis.

identical twins — monozygotic or one-egg twins.

inborn error of metabolism — a genetical defect that blocks, diverts, or otherwise alters metabolic processes, often with pathological consequences for the individual.

inbreeding — mating between relatives, especially applied to mating between first or second cousins.

incudomalleal fusion — a deformity in which the incudomalleolar joint is fused by bone; one of the most common of congenital middle ear anomalies.

inguinal hernia — protrusion of intestine through the abdominal wall in the groin area.

inversion — a reversal of the usual gene order along part of a chromosome, following breakage and reunion of noncorresponding ends after 180 degree rotation of the internal broken segment.

karyotype — the chromosomes of an individual systematically arranged from photomicrographs of a single cell's nucleus.

kyphoscoliosis — a convex backward curvature of the spine in association with scoliosis.

labyrinthitis — inflamation of the labyrinth of the inner ear (i.e., the cochlea, vestibule, or semicircular canal).

lethal genes — alleles that cause early death of the affected individual, at the stage of embryo, fetus, or infant. Such genes can never be passed on to offspring, unless they occasionally fail to penetrate. Most cases with a lethal dominant trait are, therefore, due to new mutation.

linkage — if two genetic loci are on the same chromosome, they are said to be linked.

locus — the precise position of a particular gene on a chromosome. Different forms of the gene (alleles) are found at the same position (locus) on homologous chromosomes.

Lyon hypothesis (inactive-X, phenomenon) — the genetic inactivation of all X chromosomes in excess of one, on a random basis in all cells at an early stage of embryogenesis.

lymphedema — swelling caused by the accumulation of lymph, the clear fluid present in tissues throughout the body.

macroorchidism — abnormal enlargement of the testes.

mandibular ramus — the upturned perpendicular extremity on the lateral side of the mandible.

mastoiditis — inflamation of the mastoid pinus.

maxilla — upper bone of the jaw.

meiosis — a special form of nuclear division which occurs during the formation of gametes (spermatozoa and ova) in sexually reproducing organisms. Two consecutive cell divisions, the first and second meiotic divisions, occur but only one division of the chromosomes occurs; thus, the number of chromosomes is reduced from the diploid (46) to the haploid (23) number. During meiosis, pairing of homologous chromosomes takes place, followed by chromosomal breakage and crossing over.

mesodermal — those parts of the body derived from the middle of the three primary germ layers of an embryo (e.g., skeleton, muscles).

micrognathia — underdevelopment of the chin.

micropthalmia — abnormally small size of one or both eyes.

microsomia — smallness of the body.

microtia — small or underdeveloped ears.

mitosis — a form of nuclear division in which each chromosome "splits" lengthwise (it replicates itself), one chromatid of each chromosome passing to one daughter cell and the other chromatid to the second daughter cell. Thus, each daughter cell receives the full complement of 46 chromosomes. This type of cell division is characteristic of somatic cells and of germ cells before the onset of meiosis.

monogenic (monomeric) inheritance — inheritance of a trait that is governed by a single genetic locus.

monosomy — the presence in an otherwise diploid complement of only one member of a particular chromosomal pair (2n–1).

monozygotic (monozygous) twins — twins resulting from the division into two embryos of a single zygote, following fertilization of a single ovum by a single spermatozoon (synonym: *identical* or *one-egg twins*).

mosaic — an organism that displays genotypic or phenotypic variation from cell to cell within the same tissue or genotypic variation between tissues. At least two cell lines differing in genotype or karyotype are present.

modifiers — factors that affect the expression of a gene. Modifiers may be other genes or they may be environmental factors.

mutagen — any agent that may induce mutation (or increase the rate of mutation).

mutant — a changed or mutated allele or gene; or an individual bearing such a mutant allele.

mutation — a change of a gene from one allelic form to another. Mutations are an important source of hereditary diversity. The term also is used generally to include chromosomal aberration (see also *point mutation*).

nephritis — inflammation of the kidneys.

neurofibroma — a benign neoplasm derived from nerve fibers.

nevus — an area of discolored skin that is due either to hyperpigmentation or hyperplasia of blood vessels.

nondisjunction — an abnormality of nuclear division in which a pair of newly divided chromosomes fail to "disjoin" or separate to opposite poles of the division spindle and instead both pass together to one pole. The resulting daughter cells thus contain unequal numbers of chromosomes. Nondisjunction explains the origin of many of the numerical variations of the human chromosomes. If all the cells of an individual agree in showing the same abnormal number, nondisjunction must have occurred either during the early mitotic division of the zygote followed by selection of one aneuploid line, or during meiosis in one of the parental germ cells.

oligodactyly — the presence of fewer than five digits on any one extremity.

organomegaly — enlargement of the liver or spleen.

otoadmittance — also know as *immittance*. A procedure used to assess the status of the external and the middle ear. The tests performed typically include: tympanometry, a measure of static compliance, the determination of the acoustic reflex threshold, and a measure of the reflex decay.

palpebral fissures — the slits of the eye formed by the upper and lower eyelids.

parotid gland — the salivary gland anterior to the ear.

patent ductus arteriosus (PDA) — failure of the ductus arteriosus to constrict. The ductus arteriosus is a small blood vessel connecting the pulmonary artery to the aorta in fetal life. Following birth, physiological factors cause this connection to constrict. Failure of constriction allows some of the blood to bypass the pulmonary circulation and thus, be underoxygenated.

pedigree — diagram of a family tree, showing the occurrence of one or more traits in different members of a family. The analysis of patterns of heredity is facilitated by the study of pedigrees.

penetrance — when a gene (or an allelic pair) shows an effect in the phenotype, it is said to penetrate. The penetrance of a gene is the number of individuals showing the phenotypic trait expressed as a percentage of all those possessing the gene. When a dominant gene fails to produce any effect in an individual — that is, its expressivity is nil — there is said to be a failure of penetrance; the gene has "skipped a generation." Failure of penetrance is thus the extreme degree of reduced expressivity of a gene. A dominant gene that fails to penetrate from time to time is an irregular dominant.

periventricular calcification — usually seen as tiny nodules in the brain substance close to the ventricular system, commonly as a secondary consequence of congenital infections such as cytomegalovirus or toxoplasmosis.

pharyngeal flap — surgical procedure to aid in achieving velopharyngeal closure; a flap of skin used to close most of the opening between the velum and the nasopharynx.

phenocopy — an environmentally produced change in the phenotype which mimics a genetically determined trait.

phenotype — the sum total of all observable features of a developing or developed individual (including anatomical, physiological, biochemical, and psychological makeup and disease reactions, potential or actual). The phenotype is the result of interaction between the genotype and the environment. The term may also apply to the trait produced by a single gene or several genes.

phocomelia — abnormal development of the limbs such that they appear short and close to the body.

plasmapheresis — an experimental procedure where plasma is separated from the cellular components of blood with only the cellular portion being returned. This effectively removes the plasma proteins from a parent.

pleiotropism — the production of multiple phenotypic effects by a single gene. Some cases of apparent pleiotropism may be due to a single gene operating early in embryonic development, so that many later processes are indirectly affected.

point mutation — change of a gene at a single locus (in contrast with chromosomal aberrations such as deletions and translocations).

polydactyly — extra fingers or toes.

polygenic inheritance — inheritance of a trait governed by many genes which are called polygenes or multiple factors. Each of these genes may act independently and their total effect is cumulative. Height and weight and other dimensions of the body are determined in part by polygenic inheritance (quantitative inheritance).

polymorphism — genetic polymorphism refers to the coexistence of two or more alleles in a population in frequencies too high to be explained by new mutations (e.g., the coexistence of the different blood groups or hemoglobin types in a human population).

polyneuritis — inflammation of multiple nerves.

polyploidy — the occurrence of an abnormal number of chromosomes which is an exact multiple of the haploid number, though greater than two times the haploid number. Polyploids may be triploid, tetraploid, pentaploid, hexaploid, etc., these forms being simply expressed as 3n, 4n, 5n, 6n, etc.

prenatal diagnosis — determination of the karyotype or phenotype (or sex) of a fetus, usually prior to 20 weeks of gestation. A variety of techniques, especially amniocentesis and cell culture, is employed.

proband — see *propositus.*

propositus(a) — an affected individual through whom a family is first brought to the attention of the investigator. The propositus(a) is usually indicated on a pedigree by an arrow.

ptosis — droopiness of the upper eyelid.

Q-T interval — an electrocardiographic term used to denote the distance between the QRS complex and the T-wave. This measurement reflects the electrical activity of the heart.

recessive gene — a gene that is unable to express its effect when it is present in heterozygous state (single dose) as it is dominated by its dominant allele; a recessive gene must be present in homozygous state (double dose) to express its effect. Refined methods of analysis have shown that many genes formerly thought to be completely recessive do, in fact, produce a slight in the heterozygote, that is, they are incompletely recessive.

renal dysplasia — abnormal development of the kidney or urinary tract.

retinitis pigmentosa — a hereditary condition of the retina characterized by inflammation and pigmentary infiltration of the retina.

RNA (ribose nucleic acid) — this form of nucleic acid is found in the cytoplasm and to a small extent in the chromosome. It differs both in its sugar component and in its nitrogenous bases from DNA. RNA is essential for the synthesis of proteins and acts as an intermediary, handing on the genetic information to the sequence of amino acids in the proteins.

Scheibe aplasia — this most common form of inner ear aplasia is characterized by exclusive involvement of the membranous portion of the cochlea. Specific features include atrophy of the stria vascularis, a rolling up of the tectorial membrane, and degeneration of the organ of Corti.

sclera — the white of the eye.

sex chromatin — a chromatin mass in the nucleus of interphase and early prophase cells of most mammalian species, including humans. It represents a single X chromosome which is relatively inactive in the metabolism of the cell. Females normally have sex chromatin, and thus are sex *chromatin positive;* males normally lack it, and thus are sex *chromatin negative.* (Synonyms: *Barr body, X-body.*)

sex chromosomes — the chromosomes that govern primary sex determination. In the human being, these are XX in female individuals and XY in male individuals. The distribution of these sex chromosomes governs the distribution of offspring; those who in the normal course of events receive a Y from their father and an X from their mother become males; those who receive an X from both father and mother become females. Errors may occur in the distribution of the sex chromosomes to the offspring, resulting in a variety of sexual abnormalities.

sex determination — the determination of the genetic sex of an individual by the type of sex chromosome present.

sex differentiation — the embryological development of the features of a particular sex.

sex limited — when the expression of a trait is restricted to one sex or markedly reduced in the other.

sex linkage — a form of linkage in which the gene is situated on the X or the Y chromosome. If the gene is on the nonhomologous part of the Y, holandric or male-to-male inheritance results; if the gene is on the homologous part of the X or the Y, incomplete or partial sex linkage results. If the gene is on the nonhomologous part of the X, complete X linkage results; such a gene will be passed from a heterozygous mother to half of her daughters and half of her sons, and from a father only to his daughters (to whom he gives his X chromosome).

sibs (siblings) — brothers and sisters of the same family.

sibship — a group of children resulting from the union of the same two parents.

somatic cells — all the body cells except the sex cells.

somatic mutation — occurrence of a mutation in a somatic cell; it may produce mosaic effects in the mutant individual, but it will not be transmitted to progeny.

spondylitis — inflammation of the vertebral bodies.

stenosis — a narrowing of a canal or opening (e.g., cardiac valves).

strabismus — squinting or deviation of the eyes from a parallel axis.

synchondrosis — a joining of two bones by cartilaginous material.

syncope — fainting.

syndactyly — persistent soft tissue between the fingers and toes, giving the impression of webbing.

trait — a characteristic manifested in the phenotype of an individual.

translocation — the transfer of a segment of one chromosome to another. The translocation is reciprocal when there is mutual exchange of part of a chromosome arm with that of another homologous or nonhomologous chromosome resulting from their breakage and subsequent reunion. The exchanged segments may be equal or unequal in size.

trisomy — the addition to an otherwise normal diploid complement of a member of a particular chromosome pair (2n + 1).

tympanogram — a graph depicting the compliance of the tympanic membrane as a function of changes in the amount of air pressure applied to the (sealed) external auditory meatus. In clinical settings the following classification scheme is used to describe the most common tympanometric shapes:

■ **Type A:** The point of maximum compliance occurs when the amount of pressure exerted is the same on both sides of the tympanic membrane (i.e., $+/2-50$ mm H_2O). This is characteristic of normal middle ear function.

■ **Type A$_s$:** Similar to type A with reduction in the amplitude of the response observed at the point of maximum compliance.

■ **Type AD:** The compliance of the tympanic membrane is within normal limits (i.e., $+/-50$ mm H_2O). However, the maximum amplitude of the response is so large that the peak of the response is beyond the maximum capabilities of the instrument used to display compliance.

■ **Type B:** No changes in compliance are observed with changes in the amount of air pressure applied in the external auditory meatus. This tympanogram shape can be due to the presence of fluids in the middle ear cavity or cerumen in the external auditory canal.

■ **Type C:** The point of maximum compliance can be determined from the tympanogram. However, the point of maximum compliance of the tympanic membrane is observed when there is negative air pressure in the external auditory meatus. This pattern of response is associated with poor Eustachian tube function.

tympanosclerosis — the result of a deposit of calcium on the tympanic membrane.

ventricular septal defect (VSD) — failure of complete development of the intraventricular septum. Abnormal shunting of blood can occur as a result.

vitiligo — pale patches of skin due to loss of pigment.

X chromosome — a sex chromosome that normally occurs singly in the male, but in duplicate in the female. The X comprises a nonhomologous segment and probably a homologous segment corresponding with part of the Y.

X linkage — linkage due to the presence of a gene on the X chromosome; the term is applied especially to genes on the nonhomologous segment of the X chromosome, or to traits dependent on such genes for their expression.

Y chromosome — a sex chromosome that normally occurs singly in the male, but is totally lacking in the karyotype of the female. The Y comprises of nonhomologous segment and probably a homologous segment corresponding with part of the X.

zygoma — the facial bones in the area of the temple.

zygosity — the number of zygotes from which a set of twins or higher multiple births has resulted.

zygote — a cell formed by the fusion of male and female gametes; a fertilized egg.

Subject Index

Italic page numbers refer to tables and figures.

NOTES

NOTES